MW00412995

A CAPYBARA FOR CHRISTMAS

European Travel,
Japanese Adventure,
Maximum Mayhem

*Dedicated to my wonderful family, in memory of many past adventures,
and in anticipation of many in the future.*

Copyright

CONTENTS

1. HOLIDAYS

"I can't believe we flew over the North Pole." Candi swivelled her iPhone towards me. "I snapped amazing photos from the plane window. My Instagram feed'll be the best."

"Did you take a picture of Santa?" asked Fiona. "His workshop's up there."

Candi tied her long, brown hair in a ponytail and glared at her mother. "Seriously? I'm seventeen, not seven."

Ellie sighed. "Seeing the Pole was an amazing experience, but it's so sad the Arctic sea ice is melting, and the polar bears are losing their habitat."

The queue for Frankfurt border control shuffled forward. Overhead illuminated signs separated passengers into European and non-European denominations, and announcements in German and English advised us to ensure we joined the correct line. I idly twanged the temporary barrier's seatbelt-like material, strained to recall enough high school German to impress the border agents and reflected over the events that had brought us to this point.

Several months earlier, and after three years of border closures, a threat had hung over our twin girls' ambition to visit as many countries as their age. By their fourteenth birthday, they'd travelled to seventeen nations. On their seventeenth, the needle stuck firmly at seventeen.

We needed to take immediate action, and as soon as our home country of Australia re-opened for travel, I brought up the subject at dinner.

"We'll need a long holiday if we're visiting several nations, so we should travel over the eight-week Christmas holidays," said Fiona, slicing her barbecued rump steak. She always thought practically, which was a good thing, as I could easily go camping and forget to bring a tent.

5

"Eight weeks?" I shook my head. "We can't go abroad for eight weeks. The cat'll be lonely. Poor Tiger. He'll miss attacking us."

The last tong of chips found their way onto my plate.

"Far out, Simon. I didn't mean stay away for the entire school holidays. We could go for four or five weeks. The girls must visit at least three countries to keep the goal on track."

"More than three. They've exams next year and then university; who knows when they'll travel again?"

Fiona drummed her fingers. "Several countries in December? Don't forget, it'll be winter in the Northern Hemisphere."

I tugged out my *Times Atlas of the World,* a gigantic, hardback, schooldays relic from the days when the USSR ruled Eastern Europe and Zimbabwe was still known as Rhodesia. It crashed on the table between us, and I flopped it open at a random page.

"How about Africa?" My finger poked roughly in the location of the Sahara Desert. "There are loads of countries adjoining each other there."

"I'd love to visit Africa." Fiona glanced at Candi, who was engaged in the important pursuit of showing Ellie an Instagram video of a dachshund. "We'd have to check how safe each country is for young women."

I rifled through the book and selected another page. "Central America? It'd be easy to rack up several countries there. Or the Caribbean?"

"The ticket prices are so high to the Americas now." Fiona considered my suggestion. "Hardly anyone's flying that route from Australia."

I ran my finger down the index and turned to page 47. "Europe? You and I've been there, but the girls have only visited France and Belgium. We could cover ten countries quickly."

"You must be kidding." She shivered involuntarily. "It'll be freezing at Christmas. Everyone'll say we're crazy to swap an Australian summer for a European winter. We'll need to wear Arctic survival gear to cope with the ice, fog and snow."

Candi looked up from her phone. "Did someone say snow?"

I nodded. "We were discussing travelling to new countries before you turn eighteen."

Ellie leant forwards. "Could we ski in Japan? I've always wanted to visit, ever since we learnt Japanese in primary school. Will there be any snow left, with climate change?"

I ignored her constant jibes designed to make me feel personally responsible for the imminent demise of planet Earth.

"We weren't talking about skiing specifically," said Fiona. "Dad suggested we tour around Europe so we see several countries on one trip. I said it'd be cold."

"There'll be tons of snow," I said. "France, Germany, Switzerland, Austria; they all have ski resorts."

"How many countries are there in Europe?" asked Candi. "We've been to France and Belgium already. And England, of course."

"Don't forget the rules." I tapped twice on the table. "We must spend at least one night in each country and eat a meal of the local cuisine to count it."

I opened my laptop and flicked through skyscanner.com. "Here's a flight which'd work, and it's reasonably priced. Japan Airlines into Frankfurt, returning from London. We could hire a car and drive between the airports, through Germany, Luxembourg and France.

"Germany and Luxembourg are only two new countries," said Fiona. "Not enough."

"Which part of Germany's Frankfurt in?" asked Ellie. She leant across the atlas. "Is it near Munich? I want to go to the beer halls. My friend told me the legal drinking age in Europe's sixteen when you're accompanied by parents."

"Yes!" said Candi. They high-fived.

"The last time I stayed in Munich," I said, "someone persuaded me to eat Pferdelunge. Horse's lungs."

Ellie blew out her cheeks. "Gross. Poor horse."

"What would you enjoy if we visited Europe in winter?" I asked Fiona.

"Um, touring royal palaces? And I'm overdue for an Indian takeaway; Australian curries aren't a patch on British."

"I meant in mainland Europe. Not England."

"I've travelled through all the central European countries before." She shrugged. "I've seen the main sights."

"Ye-e-s, in your early twenties, on a Contiki tour. This'll be different. Less partying and alcohol."

"Speak for yourself," said Candi. "I think there'll be plenty of partying and alcohol."

I rolled my eyes at her. "What are you looking forward to most, Candi?"

"Shopping. I need to buy a dress for next year's school formal. And I'd like to see the Christmas markets. My friend visited Europe last December, and her Instagram feed looked incredible."

"Could we include Scotland?" asked Ellie. "One more country on our tally, and I want to see bagpipers wearing kilts. I have to meet my people." She tossed her long, red hair, the colour of which strangers had commented on all her life.

"I'm sure there'll be loads of redheads," I said. "Like the movie *Brave*. Vikings with pigtails chucking cabers around left, right and centre."

I scrolled through skyscanner.com again. "There must be flights between Germany and Scotland. Oh. Here's one from Munich. We could rent a car in Frankfurt and drop it off in Bavaria. EasyJet flies from there to Edinburgh.

"Yes!" said Ellie. "I'm going to see my tribe."

I traced my finger across the atlas. "How about this? We'll fly with Japan Airlines to Frankfurt, collect a hire car and drive in a big semicircle through Germany and Luxembourg."

My family crowded around the map.

"Our route continues through France to Switzerland, east to Austria and across the German border again at Munich."

I leant back. "Then, we'll fly with EasyJet to Edinburgh, pick up another car and travel south through Scotland and England, catching up with family and friends for Christmas. That's one, two, three, four, five new countries."

"It sounds like an amazing itinerary," said Fiona. "So long as we bring enough warm clothes." She furrowed her brow and bent over the map. "There's one other nation on our travels too."

"There is?" I replaced my glasses and scanned my eyes across the atlas. "Which one? D'you mean Italy? It'd be a significant diversion."

"Nope, not Italy." Fiona pressed her finger on the jagged line separating Switzerland from Austria. "This one. Liechtenstein."

"Liechtenstein? Where is it? Move your hand; I can't see."

Fiona relocated her finger and exposed a tiny sliver. "Here. It's one of the smallest countries in the world. I visited it on my bus tour in the nineties."

I pulled my spectacles down my nose and stared at the page.

Candi leant over me. "If we spend a night in Liechtenstein, by the end of this trip, we'll have visited twenty-three countries in our lives."

"Twenty-four," I said. "The plane stops in Japan too."

"Japan?" said Ellie. "Can we book it now, Dad? I'm excited already." She grinned and hummed.

"Me too," said Candi. "My friends'll be so envious of my photos."

I turned to Fiona. "Guess we're going to Europe. And Japan."

"I'll need a new puffy coat."

"Really? You own five puffy coats."

"I'll buy a thicker one to cope with the below-freezing temperatures. We don't experience them in Australia. And some more gloves and a woolly hat."

"You'll spend your holiday shopping and visiting royal palaces; Ellie's hanging out to see the Scots clans and drink beer in Munich, and Candi wants to visit Christmas markets and add to her Instagram feed."

"What about you, Dad?" asked Ellie. "What are you looking forward to?"

I smiled at her. "Family time. And travelling again after the border closures."

Fiona held my arm. "Since we'll be away for Christmas, is there anything special you'd like to do?"

"Actually, there is." I nodded and grinned. "Remember the zoo near Bristol I found on the Internet? D'you reckon we could visit while we're in Britain? I need to tick off a bucket-list item and meet the capybara."

Capybaras had bewitched me, ever since I'd read Gerald Durrell's South American book *Three Singles to Adventure*. Essentially giant mice, I loved how they appeared sedate, gentle, even regal.

Every zoo I'd visited, all my adult life, I'd inquired if capybaras featured in their menagerie. My children grew up saying the word 'capybara' almost before the word 'cat' and, on any trip to an animal collection, our first assignment was to hunt out the capybaras.

But they'd always been hidden behind tall fences.

In the distance.

Camouflaged among lush vegetation, or asleep, concealed inside dark enclosures.

I'd never seen one close-up.

Never touched one.

Never stroked one.

One day, I'd been idly doom-scrolling through Facebook, when a schoolfriend's family picture stopped me.

I stared at my phone.

I expanded the photo with two forefingers to ensure the image wasn't fake.

It wasn't.

This boy posed with a capybara.

A real-life capybara.

He wasn't only posing with it, he hand-fed it.

This boy was hand-feeding a capybara as if it were a pet pony.

I quickly pinged my friend.

>>>Hi, Andrew. I know we haven't spoken in decades, but I've an urgent question for you. The picture of your son feeding the capybara, where was it taken?

>>>Hi, Simon. It's a zoo near Bristol, in England.

>>>What's the zoo's name?

>>>Um, I've forgotten. Chew something?

>>>Chew something? I mean, where is it? Not what the animals do.

>>>LOL. Found it. Chew Valley Animal Park.

>>>Did you need to book?

>>>I rang them the day before our visit.

>>>Cool. Thanks so much. Speak to you in another thirty years.

>>>LOL. Bye.

Fiona tapped my arm and brought me back to the present. "We could enjoy Christmas with our friends in the Lake District after Scotland," she suggested, "and then head south via your family in Bristol before dropping the rental car at Heathrow."

"And via the capybara?" I asked.

Fiona laughed and rolled her eyes. "Yes. Via your capybara."

I clenched both fists in front of my chest and grinned, as my family's discussion about Christmas markets, sumo wrestling and royal palaces blurred into the background.

Our European and Japanese holiday now included my major bucket-list item.

An encounter with an animal I'd been dreaming about forever.

And thanks to the photo in my schoolfriend's Facebook feed, I'd not only meet a capybara; I'd hand-feed one.

This trip would include the best experience of my life.

2. SANTA BABY

Japan Airlines whisked us across the globe, avoiding the Ukraine situation by crossing the North Pole. After two long flights, a four-hour stopover in Tokyo and an exchange with a polite but geographically challenged check-in lady who'd almost sent our bags to Paris in the belief the acronym FRA stood for France, we landed in Frankfurt, Germany.

"Can we count Japan as country eighteen?" asked Candi. She yawned and stretched.

"Not yet." I shook my head. "When we stop in Tokyo for five nights on the way home, you can tick Japan off."

A couple in front of us conversed with the border agents. The thump-thump of stamps on travel documents echoed from neighbouring cubicles.

"What d'you know about Germany?" I asked my family as I counted the passports in my hand for the seventeenth time to ensure I still owned four.

"Hitler came from here," said Candi. "He was the leader of the Nazi Party and dictator of Germany from 1933 to 1945. I learnt about him in politics."

"He was actually born in Austria, but, yes, he's famous, or should I say, infamous, for his terrible acts in German history. Anything else?"

"They make several brands of beer," said Fiona. "With natural ingredients."

I grinned and nodded. "German beer is particularly tasty, yes."

"You should know." Fiona puffed. "Remember the time you drank ten Löwenbräus and spent the evening in TGI Friday's toilet? So embarrassing. What a state to be in at your birthday party."

"Dad!" said Ellie.

I inspected the floor. "The girls don't need to know about that. Anyway,"—I lifted my head—"it wasn't the beer. I think that spicy chicken burger must've been dodgy."

"Right. Dodgy chicken." Fiona rolled her eyes.

Frankfurt's border agents' buzz-cut hairstyles and efficient, brisk actions reminded me I'd landed in a country I hadn't visited since I'd taken a bus tour in 1995 with 52 other young people, one of whom subsequently became my wife.

I hugged Fiona, and she gave me an odd look.

"Remember, Dad," said Ellie. "These are border guards. None of your politically incorrect *Fawlty Towers* German jokes."

Along with several hundred fellow passengers, we lingered at the stationary baggage carousel.

I bobbed up and down on my toes and grinned at my family. "You'll be proud of me on this trip. I've brought an ice scraper."

"Are you serious?" Fiona opened her eyes wide and shook her head. "Here I am worrying whether I've room to pack another coat, and you've brought an ice scraper?"

"It's tiny. And we'll be glad of it when our windscreen's frozen in Switzerland or somewhere."

"Right," she said. "What else have you brought, Mr Organised?"

"I've purchased a Spanish SIM card, so we'll always have Google Maps."

"We're not visiting Spain."

"Doesn't matter. The company assured me it'll work in every European country. We'll never be lost."

"Not like previous holidays," said Ellie. "Remember when you refused to pay Europcar for a satnav, and we burnt hundreds of litres of petrol circumnavigating Paris eight times trying to find the Marriott?"

"That won't happen this time. We'll be at tonight's accommodation in time for dinner."

"And," said Candi, "with your new SIM, you'll be able to hotspot me so I always have wifi."

13

"I'm not sure. The data package might not have enough capacity for your thousands of photos. Why didn't you buy your own SIM?"

"Because you have one. Could you hotspot me now? I need to upload the North Pole pictures."

"I haven't turned my phone on yet. I powered it off for the flight."

Fiona yawned. "What time do our bodies think it is? The clock here says 5:45 p.m."

"That's another thing I've been really organised about." I grinned and tugged a small, chrome item from my pocket.

"Woah," said Ellie. "What's that?"

"It's a digital alarm clock," I unfolded the flat, silver-coloured rectangle. Black LCD numbers flickered. "I found it in my bedside drawer."

Ellie furrowed her brow. "It looks like something from *Back to the Future.*"

"I bought it during the nineties, and its best feature is it won't connect to any wifi."

"How is that the best feature?" asked Candi. "In my opinion, that'd be the worst feature."

"It'll always tell the time in Australia, no matter where we are." I nodded and grinned. "Right now, it's"—I flipped the display around—"7:45 a.m. at home."

Fiona held her tummy. "No wonder I'm hanging out for breakfast."

We dragged our bags through Frankfurt's vast Terminal 2. The polished, tiled concourse reflected the harsh, clinical lights, and partly comprehensible announcements echoed from unseen speakers.

I swapped hands and shook my fingers. "This is agony. Why do we have so much luggage?"

"We had to bring loads of clothes," said Candi.

"What, because of the cold?"

"No, so we're not wearing the same outfits in all our photos."

"You're bloody joking." I slammed the bag on the ground. "I'm dragging this twenty-kilo holdall around Europe so your friends enjoy a better online experience?"

"We can't be unfashionable for Instagram, Dad."

Fiona tugged my arm. "I can see Hertz and Avis signs. Car rentals must be this way."

Enterprise Car Hire's doors displayed a white, laminated, A4-sized sign sellotaped to the centre. I placed both my palms on the window and peered inside.

"What does that say, Dad?" asked Ellie. She traced her fingers along the sign. "My French studies won't help me here."

"Finally, listening in Miss Iredale's class all those decades ago will come in useful." I inspected the note with my hands on my hips and smiled. "I'm not sure of the exact translation, but the gist is: the car rental office is closed."

"Yes, Simon." Fiona stared through the glass doors. "I don't think I need German lessons to understand that."

"It also says for car rental we need to take a bus to Terminal 1."

"Does it say where the bus leaves from?"

"Er, no." I swung around and glanced into a bookshop window. "Could I just pop in here a minute? I want to see if they have any books about capybaras."

"Is your German that good?" asked Fiona.

The bus arrived at Terminal 1, and I began the lengthy process of pulling all our bags off and passing them onto the kerb before the driver decided we'd spent long enough unloading and disappeared to the next stop. The weight of our luggage had increased by one children's book, entitled *Das Glückliche Capybara*, with a cartoon of a happy, smiling mummy, daddy and baby capybara on its cover.

Fiona inspected it. "Why did you buy a book suitable for a five-year-old?"

"It was the only capybara book they had. Even if I can't understand all the German words, at least I'll be able to look at the pictures."

She shook her head and stuffed it in the hand luggage.

"Guten Abend." I greeted the Enterprise staff member in Terminal 1. "Wir haben ein Auto reserviert."

15

"You are here to collect a car?" she said, in perfect, slightly accented English.

The smell of car cleaning spray accompanied a young man wearing overalls, who removed keys from a safe and marched from the office.

I gave up speaking my classroom German. "Yes. I hope you have a big one for us." I swept my arm around the bags on the floor, resembling the aftermath of a catastrophe in Kmart's luggage department.

"Your driving licence, please?"

I fished in my wallet.

"Thank you, Herr Prior. Will anyone else be driving?"

I glanced at Fiona and raised my eyebrows.

"Do you mind driving in Europe?" she asked.

"Would you like to add a satnav for fifteen euros per day?" asked the car rental lady.

"No, thank you. I've brought a European SIM, so we'll navigate with Google Maps."

"Are you sure, Dad?" asked Ellie. "Paris? Remember?"

"I'm not paying for a satnav. I've already paid for a European SIM."

The lady removed a set of keys from a ziplock bag and read a number on their tag. "We have a Peugeot for you today. It will be fine for your bags." She handed me an iPad. "Please read the terms and sign in the rectangular box."

"That's it? No paperwork?"

Candi laughed. "Dad. It's on the iPad."

I signed a wibbly version of my signature with the end of my finger, and the lady handed me the keys.

"Take lift two to level B4. Your car is in section seven, space P13. The code to exit the barrier is 0294."

I grabbed the keys and nodded once. "Lift two to level B4, section seven, space P13. Barrier code 0294. Got it."

We dragged our luggage down a concourse as long as an airport runway, and all her instructions immediately fell out of my brain.

"Which lift did she say, Fiona?"

"I don't know. She was talking to you, not me."

"Lift two," said Candi. "To level B4."

Fiona shook her head. "I'm glad someone paid attention."

We discovered lift two and descended to level B4.

"Now what?" I asked.

16

Nobody spoke.

"Does anyone remember what we do next?"

We looked at each other. Candi shrugged.

"Oh, for goodness' sake," said Fiona. "Wait here; I'll go back upstairs and ask."

She pressed the lift button and strode through the doors.

"Why don't you turn your phone on now, Dad?" said Ellie. "You should make sure your new SIM's working."

"It won't find a signal underground. I'll wait until we leave the car park."

"Where's tonight's hotel?" asked Candi.

"We're staying in a city called Mainz, a short distance outside Frankfurt. I checked before we left Australia, and we'll have no problem finding it with Google Maps."

"Oh, no," said Ellie. "I'm having Paris déjà vu."

The lift doors opened, and Fiona reappeared. "Section seven's right here. Space P13. You're standing in front of it." She pointed.

"Seriously?" I pressed a button on the car keys, and the indicator lights on a black Peugeot station wagon behind me flashed twice. The boot accepted our bags without complaining, and I smiled to myself as I remembered the driver's door opened on the left side.

I pushed myself back in the seat, pressed the start button, turned to Fiona and grinned as engine noise reverberated from the concrete walls. "We'll exit this basement car park so we've cellphone coverage, and I'll turn on the phone with my shiny, new European SIM."

"How long will it take to drive to the hotel?" asked Candi from the back seat. "I'm starving."

"Twenty minutes. I've booked a Hilton for our first two nights. I figured we'd need a treat after the long flight. This'll be our most extravagant accommodation on the entire trip, so let's make the most of it."

"I can't wait," said Fiona. "I'm looking forward to a long dip in a deep bath." She turned to me. "Remember to drive on the right."

"Yes, dear. I have done this before."

"The exit code's 0294."

"I know. You don't have to remind me of everything."

We centrifuged tight, one-lane ramps, exited the underground car park successfully and pulled into a lay-by on the far side of the barrier. Light rain fell, and cars splooshed past on an adjacent motorway.

"I have the hotel's address," I said. "Time to activate this SIM." I pressed the side button on my phone, and writing appeared on the screen.

>>*To activate SIM, enter PUK code.*

Four blank dashes showed beneath.

"Um, what's a PUK code?" I bit my lip.

"I've no idea," said Fiona. "Did you choose it when you bought the SIM?"

"I don't remember."

"Try the code you usually use. Your ATM PIN."

I entered the four digits.

>>*Incorrect code. Two attempts remaining before phone is locked.*

"What does it mean, two attempts remaining?"

"I don't know. Try my ATM PIN."

I entered Fiona's four digits.

>>*Incorrect code. One attempt remaining before phone is locked.*

"What are you trying to do?" asked Candi. "Why aren't we moving?"

"The phone's asking for a PUK code," I said, "and I don't know what that is."

"It's the code you receive when you buy a SIM. It's printed on the packaging which comes with it."

"Damn. I think I threw it in the bin at home."

"Don't enter anything else," said Fiona. "If you lock the SIM, we'll never find our way anywhere. Contact support when we reach the hotel."

"How will we find the hotel without Google Maps?"

"Here we go again," said Ellie. "Four hours of driving in circles coming up." She folded her jacket in half and lay against the window.

"I've found the Hilton in Mainz on Snap Maps, Dad," said Candi.

"Snap Maps?"

"Snapchat maps. Look." She thrust her phone in my face.

"How do they work? Are you connected to free wifi?"

"No. I think it relies on GPS."

I inspected her phone. "It's not exactly a map you can navigate by, is it? I can't see any road names. Sit in the front seat, Candi. I'll need you to tell me which way to go."

Fiona and Candi swapped seats, and we slowly pulled out of the layby.

"Don't go this way," said Fiona. She pointed at an intersection. "It says Nuremberg. That's the opposite direction."

18

"Well spotted." I swung the wheel away before I'd committed to the motorway entrance, nipped down a side road and found myself on an irreversible course into the underground car park we'd recently exited.

"Simon, back up." Fiona jabbed her thumb over her shoulder.

"I can't. There's a car behind me."

"Put it in reverse gear. Maybe he'll let you out."

BEEEEEP

"Bloody hell." I flinched. "He's hooting at me. I'll have to re-enter the car park."

"Great," said Ellie. "I knew this would happen."

I took a ticket at the barrier, and we circled the ground floor.

"Where's the exit?" I yelled as we manoeuvred around the tight turns.

"No idea. Try this ramp."

We descended to level B1 and enjoyed an interesting tour of the valet parking area. Young men wearing white shirts and black waistcoats backed expensive limousines into spaces.

"Can anyone see an exit sign?" I shouted.

"Snap Maps has stopped working," said Candi.

"I don't care about bloody Snap Maps. I want to get out of this car park."

We descended to level B2. Surprised business travellers closed the boots of their Porsches and Audis as we raced past.

I darted glances left and right. "How d'you escape from here?"

Level B3 displayed a pleasant assortment of families carrying bags, pushchairs and overcoats. I spun the wheel, and we dived down another slope.

"Level B4." I smacked the steering wheel as we passed space P13. "We're back where we started."

"What an amazing holiday this is turning out to be," said Ellie. "One hour in Europe, and we've gone nowhere."

"At least we know how to exit the car park from here."

We centrifuged the tight spirals again and rediscovered the exit barrier.

"What was the code to open the gate?"

"0294."

"0-2-9-4?" I pushed the square, silver keys. "Are you sure? It doesn't work."

"I'm sure. Try it again."

I tried again. "Nope. No good."

"Maybe you can only use it once? Try sticking your entry ticket in the slot. The one you took a minute ago."

I inserted the ticket, and the machine demanded 25 euros.

"25 euros? Is it kidding? We've been in here for ten minutes."

"Perhaps there's a minimum charge?"

Candi glanced in the side mirror. "Dad, there's a line of cars behind us."

I inserted my credit card and donated 25 euros to Frankfurt airport for the privilege of driving around in circles eight times on an exciting expedition to the lower levels. The barrier lifted.

"Here's the lay-by again. Candi, is Snap Maps working?"

"Um, kind of. We need to join the main road."

"The road sign says it goes to Nuremberg. Oh, and the other way says Wiesbaden."

"Pick Wiesbaden," said Fiona. "We don't want Nuremberg. That's on the way to Munich."

"Aren't we going to Munich?" asked Ellie. "The beer city?"

"Yes, but not for another two weeks."

We joined the freeway to Wiesbaden and drove into the dark. The motorway didn't benefit from streetlamps, and cars whizzed past at speeds I hadn't experienced in Australia. I flinched as each one overtook us, and I leant forward to peer at the road.

"It feels weird sitting on the wrong side of the car with no steering wheel," said Candi. "I keep pushing an imaginary brake."

"Where does Snapchat say we should go?"

"Not Snapchat. Snap Maps."

"Whatever it's called. Which direction?"

"Um, it doesn't show me at the moment."

"Great. We could be heading anywhere."

"Dad," said Ellie, from the rear seat. "We've just passed an exit saying Mainz."

"Bloody hell. Why didn't you tell me?"

"I forgot we were headed there until we passed the sign."

"It would help if you listened."

"Calm down, Simon," said Fiona. "Look. Here's another Mainz sign. Come off here."

I swung the wheel to the right, and we navigated our way through roads of diminishing size before crossing a bridge and passing a sign saying 'Willkommen in Mainz (Welcome to Mainz)'.

"There," I said. "That wasn't too hard, was it?" I gripped the steering wheel. "Now to find the Hilton."

Candi spread her fingers across her phone's screen. "Snap Maps says the Hilton's on the Rhine, so if we follow the river, we'll find it."

We entered the centre of town, dodging around cars swerving across the street and tooting their horns in a constant cacophony.

Fiona leant forward and yelled in my ear. "Simon, watch out. Wow, the Germans are terrible drivers." She watched a man lean from the window of a weaving car trailing a red banner with a green star.

"Which country's flag's that?" I asked. "It's not Germany's. That's black, red and gold."

"Morocco?" said Candi. "They played Portugal in the World Cup tonight. The man holding it looks North African. They must've won."

The further we drove into Mainz, the more Moroccans yelled, car horns klaxoned and flags streamed.

"Dad, there." Candi pointed between a group of men letting off fireworks on the pavement and a queue of tooting cars. "It's the Hilton. I told you we could find our way with Snap Maps."

I swung into the hotel's opulent driveway as if we'd arrived at Blake Carrington's house in *Dynasty* and tugged the handbrake to stop us directly in front of the modern, glass-fronted entrance. A uniformed porter briskly opened our doors, and we stepped out. Gigantic, potted palm trees rustled in the breeze as a second staff member wheeled a gold trolley towards our car.

I spread my arms wide like a biblical prophet addressing his disciples. "As I said, I've booked an amazing hotel to start our holiday. Welcome to luxury."

"This place looks incredible," said Fiona. She stared upwards through the glass and steel frontage and grinned. "Look at the chandelier in the atrium. Well done, Simon. I can't wait to find our room, run a nice, hot bath and wrap myself in a luscious, crisp Hilton dressing gown."

"I've already picked up free Hilton wifi," said Candi. "It's really fast."

Ellie smiled. "The plants in reception are so leafy. They'll offset some of the carbon debt we created driving here."

I grinned and wiggled my eyebrows. "See. I know what I'm doing sometimes."

The porter arranged our bags on a trolley, and we followed him through the gold-framed entrance doors into a white, marble-tiled atrium surrounded by luxurious indoor foliage. A pianist dressed in a dinner jacket and bow tie played a Burt Bacharach-type version of *Santa Baby*, under a two-storey Christmas tree decked in gold trimmings. The receptionist grinned at me like a toothpaste advertisement.

"Guten Abend," I said. "Wir haben eine Reservierung (We have a reservation)."

"English?" said the receptionist, immaculately dressed in a black suit with a grey cravat.

"Australian, actually."

"Your name, please?"

"Prior."

He tapped on his computer, paused and frowned.

"Could you spell for me, please?"

"P-R-I-O-R."

He scrolled his mouse and shook his head. "Sorry, sir. There is no reservation for Prior."

3. SNOWFLAKES

I leant forward with both hands on his counter. "What d'you mean, there's no reservation for Prior? There must be. I made it through booking.com." I turned to Fiona. "Did you print out the details?"

"Yep, I always do." She tugged an envelope from her hand luggage and extracted a sheet of paper.

I handed it to the receptionist. "Our reservation. One double room, one twin room, and the date is today." My finger pressed on the text which proved my statement.

He scanned the printout.

"I see the problem, sir. This is the Hilton Mainz. You have booked the Hilton Mainz City. An easy mistake. There are two."

"Oh. Is it far?"

"No. Five minutes' drive. Up that street." He pointed out of the doors and across the road.

As we were no longer valued guests, we dragged our bags out by ourselves, while the porters busied themselves with more important tasks, such as standing and watching us.

"Bye bye, lovely hotel," said Candi.

"Don't worry," I said. "The other Hilton will be even nicer."

I opened the Peugeot and reloaded the luggage.

"Damn," said Fiona, slumping back into her seat. "I was looking forward to a hot bath. Isn't it stupid, two hotels in the same city, with almost identical names?"

"I've located the other Hilton on Snap Maps, Dad," said Candi. "It's five hundred metres away, in the centre of the old town."

"Great," said Ellie. "We'll be there in five minutes."

We headed up the street the receptionist had indicated.

"Look." Ellie pointed. "A Christmas market. Our first. Let's drop our bags and head there."

Jubilant German market-goers stood at tall tables in front of brightly lit stalls, which dispensed food, drink and knick-knacks. Oompah music played, glasses clinked and a man wearing traditional costume raised his beer stein to our car as we passed.

Ellie grinned and waved back. "This is so exciting," she said. "I can't wait to explore country number eighteen. Hurry up and find this hotel."

"We've passed it," said Candi. "It's behind us."

"We can't have." I furrowed my brow and glanced over my shoulder. "Did you see anything which looked like a Hilton?"

"Nope," said Candi. "Turn right here."

"It's a one-way street," called Fiona, from the back. "And you're driving the wrong way."

"I can't turn around now. We'll have to hope no-one comes from the other direction."

"Go to the end and turn right again," said Candi.

We shot through narrow streets featuring impressive five-storey stone buildings on both sides. Cars parked half on pavements, and dim streetlights shone through the thin fog.

"Now what?" I asked, as we reached the end of the street.

"Don't know," said Candi. "We've passed it again."

"Dad," said Ellie. "This BMW wants to come in. You'll have to pull out."

I turned right, and we passed the Christmas market again. The traditionally dressed man lifted his glass a second time and waved.

"We're going around in circles," said Ellie.

"I know. Your sister's navigating."

"Don't blame me," said Candi. "You're the one who can't make your SIM work."

"Where does your map thing say the hotel is now?"

"On our right."

"It's always on our right."

I slowed down, and Candi pointed. "Turn up here, Dad. The hotel's on that street."

"I can't. It's for trams."

"Take the next one. It goes directly behind the hotel."

We circled the entire town the other way, passing the happy Germans drinking and conversing in their joyful little groups at the Christmas Market once more. I wanted to stick two fingers up at the waving man, then quickly lowered my hand before Fiona observed my gesture.

"We've passed it again," said Candi.

"I'm sick of going around in spirals." Fiona pointed at a sign. "Here's an underground garage. Leave the car in it, and we'll search on foot. We'll never find the hotel with all these one-way streets and narrow, blocked off routes."

"But we'll have to pay for parking."

"I don't care." She folded her arms. "Drive in. I'm not spending a single minute more in this car."

We entered the underground car park, took a ticket at the barrier and reversed into a space.

Candi showed me her phone. "Snap Maps says we're here. At the hotel."

"Snap Maps is rubbish. We're not in the hotel. We're in a garage. It's misled us all along."

Stark lights illuminated scattered, luxury, German vehicles. An internationally familiar smell of dried urine emanated from concrete stairs.

"Come on," said Fiona. "Let's nip upstairs and see where we are."

We ascended four flights of steps and found ourselves in a small, lawned area, with decorative lampposts illuminating the perimeter. Groups of teenagers sat on park benches, chatting and swigging from cans. Banana-flavour vape smoke wafted towards us.

A six-storey, concrete, 1950s, brutalist building overlooked the park.

The Hilton Mainz City.

"I told you we were in the hotel," said Candi. "Snap Maps was right."

I gazed at the Hilton as if it had intentionally concealed itself. "Okay, okay. Let's leave the car where it is and grab the luggage."

25

Ellie puffed. "Three hours of holiday wasted."

The Hilton Mainz City was significantly further down Hilton Group's refurbishment priorities than the opulent, riverside, glass-fronted Hilton Mainz we'd failed to check into.

"Guten Abend," I announced, repeating my earlier greeting. "Wir haben eine reservierung."

I gazed around the reception area, which reminded me of a scene from a 1970s Burt Reynolds movie. A cigarette machine with a life-size photo of a beautiful model puffing on a Marlboro completed the time hop. My teeth clenched, and I sucked in a breath.

"Guten Abend," said the receptionist. "English?"

"Australian, actually."

His shirt needed ironing. Possibly replacing.

"Your name, please?"

"Prior. P-R-I-O-R."

"Ah, Herr Prior. We have been expecting you. We had a call from the other Hilton two hours ago. Were you lost?"

Ellie leant heavily on Fiona's shoulder.

"Lost is an understatement." I sighed. "Could we have our room keys, please? We're exhausted."

"Certainly. You have a double room and a twin room, next to each other. Rooms 605 and 606 on the sixth floor. Please sign here."

"This lift stinks," said Candi. She held her nose and inspected the frayed, faded, paisley-patterned carpet.

"I thought you'd booked a luxury hotel for our first two nights," said Ellie.

Fiona ran a finger along the lift's handrail and wrinkled her nose.

"The rooms'll be fine," I said. "Even if the common areas appear to, um, need updating. It won't be long before we're lying in our soft, comfortable beds."

The lift creaked alarmingly as it ascended, as if level six was ambitious for its capabilities.

I leant my shoulder against the door of room 605 and scraped it across the buff-coloured carpet. Ellie shoved room 606 open. The two were mirror images of each other and had been since their last refurbishment in approximately 1976.

"This is a Hilton?" asked Ellie. She surveyed the orangey-brown colour scheme and puffed out her cheeks.

"Um, yes."

"It's not a very good one."

Candi entered the room and recoiled. "There must be a law compelling hotels to provide accommodation to a standard described."

"I know. I'll be hesitant about booking a Hilton again. They don't seem to be consistent. Unpack your bags, and prepare for bed, I suppose. It's nine o'clock." I flicked open the plastic alarm clock. "Although it's not quite lunchtime in Australia."

"This room smells," said Fiona. "It's musty." She twitched her nose in the air like Samantha in *Bewitched*.

I attempted to open the window, but the last time anyone had taken a paintbrush to the frame, they'd sealed it closed, forever denying us the opportunity to enjoy the fresh air of central Mainz. Fiona ran a bath, and I anticipated sitting in bed with a cup of tea and opening my capybara picture book, when someone knocked at our door.

"Maybe it's the management moving us to a better room," Fiona called from the bathroom.

"That'd be nice." I opened the door to reveal Candi brandishing a piece of paper.

"I found this in my bag," she said. "Is it what you were looking for?"

"What is it?"

"I think it's the packaging from your SIM. There's a four-digit code on the front."

"Give it to me, quick."

I snatched it from her and entered the code into the phone. The familiar Samsung start-up sequence began.

"Yes!" I grinned and performed a brief happy dance. "Well done, Candi. I've no idea how it came to be in your bag."

"Does the SIM work now?"

"The welcome screen's lit up with all the icons."

I attempted to log into Facebook.

"Um, no. There's still no connection. Can you help?"

I passed Candi the phone, while Fiona shouted from the bathroom. "The water won't stay in the bath. The plug's too small for the plughole."

"You have wifi," said Candi, "but not mobile data. It can't find an access point. There must be a setting missing."

"I'll email SIM support before I go to bed. Oh, and could I use your kettle? Ours won't boil."

I banged on the girls' door in the morning. Ellie opened it a crack.

"Quick! Quick," I barged in. "Look out of your window."

"What?" said a lump in Candi's bed. "Go away. What time is it?"

"Seven o'clock. And guess what?"

"There's been a mix-up and we're returning to the nice hotel?" said Ellie, as she rubbed her eyes.

"Even better. Come to the window, now."

"This better be good, Dad." Ellie shuffled across the room and pulled the curtains back. She gasped. "Candi, quick. It's snowed."

"You're joking," said Candi. I hadn't seen her jump out of bed so fast since the day I'd hidden a toy spider under her pillow.

She took several pictures of the car park. "Let's snap some shots in the snow," she said. "This'll be great for our feeds."

They threw clothes on and ran out of the door. I laughed, as I remembered my own childhood excitement at seeing snow from my bedroom window and realised this would probably be the first time my girls had seen snow in city streets.

Fiona and I followed and found them posing for each other's pictures, catching flakes on their tongues.

"Dad," said Ellie. "I tasted a snowflake."

Candi scraped up enough to create a tiny snowball, which failed to fly as far as Ellie's head.

I grabbed hold of my wife and skipped into the little park above the car garage as if we were starring in *It's a Wonderful Life*. The snow settled on our shoulders, and I picked her up and spun her around. "This is so special. Real, white Christmas holidays with real, white snowflakes."

I set her down, and she brushed off her clothes.

"Guess what," I said. "I finished my capybara book last night."

"I'm not surprised. There was only one word per page, and they were all in German."

"Um, yes. I'll have a trawl through Amazon later and find another one for the kindle."

Fiona grinned and rolled her eyes.

"And there's some other great news overnight too," I announced. "SIM support emailed with the settings we need, and it's working. We'll never be lost again. I've already dropped a pin in Google Maps so when we explore, we'll be able to find our way back, even with all the one-way streets and barriers."

"I think," said Fiona, "we'll leave the car in the underground car park today and walk everywhere in Mainz. I'd enjoy a day not sitting in a moving seat."

"Today," I explained, as we attempted to compensate for the poor-quality accommodation by munching our way through significantly more plates of buffet breakfast than any human could ever need, "we'll explore Mainz, and I want to visit the Gutenberg Museum." I sipped my coffee and smelt the air as a server inserted a tray of fresh bacon into the bain-marie.

"Great," said Candi. "Museums. Is that what this holiday's about?"

I ignored her. "When I booked this hotel, Mum researched local attractions, and we discovered the first printing press was invented here by German inventor Johannes Gutenberg. Five hundred years after his birth, a group of Mainz people founded the Gutenberg Museum in this, his hometown. As a writer, this is a pilgrimage for me."

Ellie finished her third bowl of fruit and yoghurt and placed sliced cheese on bread. "After we endure the museum," she asked, "could we visit the Christmas markets and try glühwein?"

"Of course. They might not be open until the evening. We'll ask someone."

"Your German practice isn't going too well so far, Dad," said Candi. "Every time you've said 'hello' to someone in German, they've immediately answered in almost flawless English."

"All right, all right." I folded my arms. "Hotel receptionists and car rental agents speak foreign languages fluently. I'll discover how good my German is by conversing with someone who speaks nothing else."

Immediately we strolled into town, I put this theory into practice.

"Is this the Christmas market, Dad?" asked Ellie, as we meandered through scattered wooden huts dispersed across a central square, all of which stood firmly shuttered.

I glanced around the scene. "Um, it might be. I'll ask this chap."

A short, elderly man wearing a brown, shabby, worker's jacket and a flat cap swept the cobbles.

I addressed him. "Guten morgen, mein herr. (Good morning, sir)"

He looked up and grunted.

I continued with my German language demonstration. "Ist das der Weihnachtsmarkt? (Is this the Christmas market?)"

He grunted again, mumbled something and pointed behind me. As I had no idea what this intimated, I persisted.

"Wann öffnet bitte der Weihnachtsmarkt (what time does the market open, please)?"

He emitted a third grunt and returned to his broom.

"Great job, Dad," said Candi. She laughed. "Excellent German."

"Maybe he was deaf?"

We strolled further through the streets. The snow on the ground, coupled with the old European buildings felt as if we were ambling through a Pieter Bruegel painting.

We discovered the museum behind the market where I'd attempted to gain directions from the unhelpful street sweeper, and Fiona pushed open the glass door of the contemporary building.

"I can't wait to see the first ever printing press," I said, staring around the high-ceilinged entrance. I paid the entrance fee as quickly as I could and charged up a flight of stairs.

The first floor featured several replica presses, a presentation about the history of printing and glass cases containing old books.

I rushed from display to display reading exhibit label after exhibit label. "Which one's the original?" I asked Fiona.

"I've no idea. Why don't you ask this guide?"

A man with a badge stood in the corner. "Wo ist bitte die Gutenbergpresse (where is the Gutenberg press, please)? I've come all the way from Australia to see it."

His mouth formed a straight line. "Sorry, sir. You have had a wasted journey. It is not here."

4. O TANNENBAUM

I stood in front of the museum guide with my mouth open.

"Seriously?" My shoulders slumped. "I've come from Australia to see the original Gutenberg Press, and it's not here. Where is it?"

"Nobody knows. It may have been destroyed in a fire. There are several replicas showing what it could have looked like."

"Right. Great. Thank you."

I returned to Fiona. "The original press was destroyed. Bloody hell. I really wanted to see it. Where are the girls?"

"They've latched on to a tour group, but it's in French, so I can't understand it."

"Excellent. They can practise for their oral exams next year. I didn't think they'd be hearing French until we reached Luxembourg."

Candi and Ellie stood with a group of people. They were the youngest by about fifty years. At the front of the group, an Einstein-lookalike spoke rapid French, accompanied by enthusiastic, explanatory gesticulations.

"Can you understand what he's saying?" I whispered in Candi's ear.

"Some of it. Apparently, the books in this case are rare. Old Bibles or something."

"These are Gutenberg Bibles?"

She shrugged. "Dunno. Maybe."

"Candi, d'you realise, these are the rarest Bibles in the world."

"So?"

"Have some appreciation for history. You'll never see another Bible this old."

"They should buy some new ones. They look tatty."

I shook my head. "You teenagers have no respect for the past."

The Christmas Market had opened by the time we left the museum, and we wandered between stalls selling mementos, packaged snacks and dolls dressed in traditional clothes. I smiled as I inhaled the essence of gingerbread combined with a festive burning smell which reminded me of a workman's brazier.

The tradition of Weihnachtsmarkts, or Christmas markets began in Germany centuries ago. Traditionally spanning the four weeks of Advent immediately prior to Christmas, they always include a Nativity Scene which is frequently life-size, glühwein, a hot, red, alcoholic drink with optional potent spirits, and sausages with assorted-flavour sauces, none of which are healthy. Although the markets open during the day, the festivities really begin after dark when crowds appear, and the masses of white, twinkly lights illuminating these gatherings are switched on.

"I'm hungry," said Candi.

"You can't be." Fiona shook her head. "You had eight breakfasts three hours ago."

"Let's buy some chips with mayonnaise," I said. "It's the traditional way to eat them in Germany."

"Yuck." Fiona puffed out her cheeks. "You can't beat Heinz tomato ketchup."

"We must eat local dishes, remember?"

"Can we try glühwein?" asked Ellie. "That's local."

"At lunchtime? You'll be asleep directly afterwards."

"I want to sleep now. What time is it in Australia?"

I pulled the little alarm clock from my pocket. "Thanks to my low-tech device, I can tell you the time at home is 10:00 p.m."

"No wonder I'm tired."

Chips with mayonnaise, glühweins and hot chocolates with whipped cream later, we arrived back at the Hilton.

"Good afternoon, sir," said the receptionist. "Is everything all right with your stay?"

"Um, no, not really. Our kettle's broken, the window won't open, and the bath plug doesn't fit the bath. And the rooms smell funny. Apart from that, it's perfect."

"There is no maintenance at weekends. Do not worry. They will fix the problems on Monday."

"Monday?" I turned both palms up. "We leave on Monday."

"Sorry, sir."

"So much for the luxury hotel," said Ellie, as we entered the creaky lift, returned to our rooms and lay down for a nap.

The Christmas Market by night broadcast a different atmosphere. Sparkling lights draped across the town square, and Oompah music competed with the sound of a merry-go-round spinning laughing children. Germans pushed past each other to reach the stalls, leant at little tables drinking glühwein and queued ten deep for sausages. We paused at the edge of the action and sought the best place to plunge into the scrum.

"Don't become separated," I instructed, as I darted glances through the crowd and held the pocket containing my phone. "We'll never find each other again."

"Could we buy food now, Dad?" asked Candi. "I'm starving."

"I hate these hordes," said Ellie, as someone elbowed her in the side.

"This is ridiculous," said Fiona. "Let's find the other market."

"What other market?" I asked. "This is the only one."

"The other market," said Fiona. "The one last night."

"Last night? We didn't go to any markets last night."

"We drove past it about fifty times. The one we saw while searching for the Hilton, with the happy waving man in traditional dress."

"Oh, that market. Um, d'you know how to find it?"

"Yes. It's two streets from the hotel."

Fiona found the smaller, less-crowded market and, a few minutes later, we gathered around an upturned wine barrel, drinking glühwein, eating sausages and chips with mayonnaise, and picking at a potato-with-garlic dish I'd decided required sampling.

"This is how Christmas is supposed to be," I said, as I dipped another chip in my mayonnaise. "Hot food, hot wine and cold noses. Not barbecues on the beach and salads." I smiled and hummed along with background music playing *O Tannenbaum*.

"I like it," said Ellie. "The buildings look so pretty in the snow. Is this how Christmas was when you were a little boy?"

I formed a steeple with my fingers. "Believe it or not, though I grew up in England, I've never seen a white Christmas. We didn't have them in the South."

"I'm loving the drinking age is sixteen here," said Candi. "They should change the law in Australia." She slurped her glühwein and posed for another Snapchat photo.

"These glasses are beautiful." Fiona admired the transparent tankard her drink had arrived in.

"I've decided I like country number eighteen," said Ellie.

"Me too," said Candi. "Um, could we buy another round?"

"Why did I eat that third bowl of Coco Pops?" I asked, as we squeezed ourselves into the rental car the following morning.

"At least we had our money's worth from the Hilton," said Ellie. "The breakfast made up for the stinky rooms. Although, if I don't see sliced ham and cheese for a week, I won't mind."

"Where are we staying tonight, Dad?" asked Candi. "Will it be as good as the first Hilton?"

"Um, no. Once we cross the border into Luxembourg, we must find the city centre backpacker's hostel. It'll be basic, but it should be clean, and we won't feel ripped off."

"This'll be a great experience for you girls," said Fiona. "A taste of real travelling. You might do it by yourselves one day."

"I don't want to travel by myself," said Candi. "I'd have to pay for everything."

"Will we be lost again and drive around in circles for two hours?" asked Ellie.

"We are not becoming lost today," I said. "The SIM works and Google Maps works. All I have to do"—I picked up my phone—"is enter: 2, Rue du Fort Olisy."

"Yay, French words," she said. "I can practise for school."

I typed the address. "Brilliant, predictive text completed it. Isn't technology wonderful? Two hours, nineteen minutes journey time."

"Are we travelling on the roads where you're allowed to drive as fast as you like?" asked Candi.

"The autobahns? I'm not sure."

"How fast will you speed if we are?"

"Um, however quickly this Peugeot goes. It's not a Ferrari. We'll be there by lunchtime."

"Good. I'll be hungry by then."

I rolled my eyes and pressed the car's start button.

"Proceed to the end of the road, then turn right," instructed the phone.

"Wow," I said. "The Google Maps lady still sounds Australian."

"Duh, Dad," said Candi. "Your Google account's in Australia."

"I know, but we're in a French car, with a phone connected to a German mobile provider via a Spanish SIM card. I expected a Marlene Dietrich voice, but she sounds like Kylie Minogue. Take us to Luxembourg, Kylie."

We joined the freeway and headed away from the worst Hilton in the world.

"Yaay, country number nineteen," said Ellie, as we passed a blue 'Luxembourg' sign, bordered by the twelve stars of the European Union. She opened her diary, grinned and ticked a box.

"Do you realise," I announced, holding up my right finger, "the four of us have visited Luxembourg before?"

"Wait, what?" said Ellie. "This isn't our nineteenth country?" Her pencil poised ready to cross through her previous tick.

"Dad doesn't mean you've seen it before," said Fiona. "But I suppose we've all been here, in a manner of speaking."

"Stop talking in riddles," said Candi. "Tell us what you're really saying."

I cleared my throat. "When we lived in England, shortly before you were born, we wanted to visit a new country. Mum couldn't fly, as she was thirty-two weeks pregnant. So, we drove to the only country within a reasonable distance of London we hadn't seen yet. There's a photo somewhere of Mum in Luxembourg with this vast lump of twins sticking out in front of her."

"We had a wonderful holiday," said Fiona. She lay her hand over mine. "Looking back, we were crazy to drive all that distance. I might've gone into labour here."

"You mean we would've been born Luxembourgish?" asked Ellie. She leant forward between the seats. "Luxembourgian? Luxemites?"

"What?" said Candi, lifting her head from her phone. "We could've had European passports as well as British, New Zealand and Australian? Why didn't you stay here?"

"Um, it wouldn't have been practical. Think yourselves lucky you've three passports. Most people have one. So, what d'you girls know about Luxembourg?"

"It's the seat of the highest judicial authority in Europe," said Candi. "We studied it in politics."

"It's one of the smallest countries," said Ellie.

"It is," I said. "It squishes between the borders of Belgium, France and Germany, with a population of over 500,000, all of whom are millionaires."

"Seriously?" asked Candi.

"Okay, I'm exaggerating, but the country's one of the richest in the world."

"Exit the freeway at the next junction," announced Kylie, the navigator.

Fiona frowned and glanced left and right. "Why is she asking you to come off here, when the signs to Luxembourg City indicate we continue on the motorway?"

"No idea. Maybe she knows a shortcut."

"Here we go," said Ellie. "Lost again."

We exited the motorway, turned onto a two-lane road which rapidly became narrower and entered a small village. A horse poked its head over a gate as we passed, and the smell of cow manure penetrated the car's air vents.

I gripped the wheel and grinned. "Google Maps says we'll be there in eight minutes. Are we all ready for the hostelling experience?"

"This can't be the right way," said Fiona, shaking her head.

"Turn left, then turn right," announced Kylie, optimistically. We traversed the village high street and headed up a single-track road between farmhouses.

"There's no hostel up here," said Fiona. "Pull over and check."

"Let's at least reach where she's taking us."

"Take the next left," continued Kylie, enthusiastically.

I pulled onto the verge to avoid a head on collision with a tractor. The farmer perched upon it regarded us incredulously.

"There's no way this is correct," said Fiona, as I slowed down, and the sides of the lane closed in. Spiky bushes scraped against the doors of the Peugeot. We were probably the first family car to ascend this route in decades. Possibly ever.

"I can't reverse now. We'll have to find somewhere to turn around."

The lane wound up and up. Fields on both sides lay winter-vacant; whatever crop they usually grew had been harvested months previously. After several minutes of climbing, we arrived at a crossroads on a plateau. The view extended for miles, but no hostel materialised. No buildings showed themselves at all.

"You have arrived," concluded Kylie, satisfied with her achievement.

"Where are we, Dad?" asked Ellie. "This is the middle of nowhere. We're in a field."

5. SCHNAPPS

I shaded my eyes and gazed in a circle. Rows of bare trees topped rolling hills extending to the horizon, and stalks of winter grass bent in a constant, strong breeze.

"This doesn't make sense," I said. "Kylie took us exactly where I asked her to. Fiona, d'you have the printout of the hostel address? I'll double check it."

Fiona passed me a sheet of paper.

"2, Rue du Fort Olisy, Luxembourg. It's the correct address. We're here."

Ellie snatched my phone. "Dad, you didn't enter '2, Rue du Fort Olisy'. You entered '2, Rue de la Montagne'. Mountain Road."

"Oh. How did that happen?"

"Your predictive text? I'll punch in the correct address." She tapped on the screen. "Okay, half an hour's drive. It must be on the other side of Luxembourg, given the size of the country."

"Perform a U-turn where possible," advised Kylie, happily.

Multiple tunnels and motorways later, we arrived in Luxembourg City.

"Turn left," persuaded Kylie.

Fiona grabbed my arm. "Simon, stop. This isn't right. It's another tiny lane."

I paused, to allow a car to exit the side road. "It is. The hostel's along here."

"You said that up the mountain."

The narrow avenue meandered through terraced, stone homes whose front doors opened directly onto the pavement. Ahead, the tall arches of an imposing aqueduct curved over the route. I pulled over and winced as a truck thundered past in the opposite direction.

39

"Turn right," instructed Kylie, and immediately in front of us stood a stone building with a sign advertising: 'Youth Hostel—Luxembourg City.'

"You have arrived," repeated Kylie.

And this time, she was right.

"This," announced Ellie, "is the smallest room I've ever slept in."

We followed her into a square cubicle containing four bunks in an L-shape shoved against the walls. She dropped her bag and her shoulders slumped.

"And," said Candi, "we even have to make our own beds." She flung armfuls of sheets and pillowcases on the floor.

"It'll give you practice for making your bed at home," said Fiona. "You need it."

I rested my arms on the window ledge. The view comprised the high aqueduct, and a path bordered by railings and streetlights wound up a hill adjacent to it. A radiator under the window created hot, stuffy air, and I loosened my jacket. "Yep, this is what backpacking is like. Your mother and I used to stay in these places when we travelled in our twenties. I'm sure when you're older you'll do the same."

"Not if I can help it," said Candi. "I'll marry a rich man."

Fiona wiped her finger along the windowsill. "It's cleaner than the Hilton."

"That wouldn't be hard," said Ellie. "The city dump would be cleaner than the Hilton."

Fiona stuffed a pillow into its case. "Let's make the beds, unpack what we need for the night and head out to explore."

"How are we going to unpack?" asked Ellie. "There's no space for our bags."

"You're too accustomed to five-star hotels." I puffed and waved the back of my hand.

"The Hilton wasn't exactly five-star."

Fiona inspected under the beds. "There's a spot down here for your bags, with a cage where you can attach your own padlock. It's useful if you're sharing with people you've never met before."

"What?" Candi slowly swivelled her head. "I'd have to share a room this size with people I'd never met before?"

"Yes, but it's fun; you make friends. Dad and I still keep up with people we met backpacking."

"I'm showering before we go anywhere," said Ellie. "Where's the towels?"

"Oh, didn't they give us any?" I inspected the pile of linen Candi had dumped. "Candi, could you return downstairs and grab some? It'll give you a chance to practice your French."

"Sure. If you make my bed."

She exited, and I rolled my eyes.

One minute later, Candi returned with no towels.

"Can you come with me, Dad? They want twelve euros deposit. I've never stayed anywhere where you have to rent towels. This place is basic."

The man behind the desk at the Luxembourg Tourist Information Centre looked exactly like a Luxembourger should. If someone asked me to draw a man from Luxembourg (and I can't imagine this would ever happen), this man was exactly who I'd draw.

Part German, part French, a jolly, rosy-cheeked face topped his short, barrel-shaped body. He had luxurious brown hair and a large, Gallic moustache, but wore semi-formal, smart-casual wear, as you would imagine a man from Berlin might sport to visit the seaside.

"Welcome," he said, ebulliently. "Willkommen. Bienvenue."

The warmth of the information centre and the sight of a tall, brightly lit Christmas tree standing in the window brought a smile to my face. I recalled the previous time Fiona and I had visited Luxembourg, when we'd enjoyed complicated conversations with hoteliers, waiters and shop staff where every sentence contained three languages, and yet everybody could somehow understand each other.

I stood in front of his counter. "Hello. We're staying in Luxembourg this evening, and we were wondering what the best things were for us to do."

The man glanced at a wall clock. "Quelle dommage. Everything will be geschlossen now."

I realised he'd explained the attractions were closed.

"Are you sure you can't stay for another day? You could visit the Groussherzogleche Palais"—he handed me a leaflet—"or the Grand Duke Jean Museum of Modern Art?" He thrust a further publication into my hands.

"Ah, um, well…" I began.

His hands rubbed together as he warmed to his sales pitch. "Then there's the Nationalmusée fir Geschicht a Konscht, the Galerie d'Art Contemporain Am Tunnel and the Musée d'histoire de la Ville de Luxembourg."

Several more pamphlets joined the collection.

"Sorry," I said. "We're on a whirlwind trip through Europe."

"If you are here only for the evening, you could visit the Weihnachtsmarkt?" he suggested. "The Christmas market?"

"Um, yes. We haven't been to one of them for, ooh, twenty-four hours. Whereabouts is it?"

He led me to the window and pointed through a stone archway.

"This Christmas market is exactly the same as last night's one," said Candi, as we strolled past wooden stalls buried in decorations. "They have the same trinkets for sale." She stuffed her hands in her pockets and slouched.

"Even though we're in a different country," I said, "we're only two hundred kilometres from Mainz."

Fiona shivered. "I'm freezing. Let's buy glühwein."

We paused outside a stall where people collected glasses of steaming, maroon liquid.

"Look," said Ellie. "Behind the bar. You can sit inside. We'll be warmer in there."

"Great," said Fiona. "I don't think I can survive another second in this temperature. How do the locals manage?"

"Maybe they're used to it?"

Inside the wooden hut, tall tables had been provided for guests to lean on. Red and silver Christmas decorations ran down the walls, interspersed with fake candles and spotty curtains framing steamed-up windows. Fiona had hoped for a roaring fire, but this detail had unfortunately been omitted.

"It feels weird being inside, with our hats, coats and scarves on." I hugged Fiona and rubbed her shoulders.

"And there's no free wifi," said Candi. She clonked her phone on the table.

"There's a glühwein menu," said Fiona, picking up a small, laminated card. "I thought glühwein was glühwein."

I read from a larger version of the same menu affixed to the wall. "Ah. I think you'll enjoy this place. They have glühwein with schnapps in it. Various flavours."

"What's schnapps?" asked Ellie.

"Something you're not adding to your drinking repertoire."

After Fiona defrosted with a schnapps glühwein and the rest of us with un-schnappsed glühweins, we ventured out of the hut and discovered the temperature had dropped another few degrees.

"What about our traditional meal?" asked Candi. "We need to eat one to count this in our list of countries. Has anyone seen a Luxembourgian restaurant?"

"We'll eat at the Christmas market." I indicated a nearby stall, where people queued for hot food. "Those sausages look traditional."

"They're the same as the ones we ate last night in Germany," said Candi.

Ellie craned her neck to look. "Maybe Luxembourg cuisine is identical to German cuisine?"

"There's a lot of sausage and bread in Northern Europe," said Fiona.

After a traditionally stodgy Christmas market dinner, we returned to the backpackers. The girls climbed up into their top bunks, and the glow of their mobile phones reflected from their faces. Fiona snuggled in the bottom bunk with her hot water bottle and flicked through leaflets the tourist information man had given us, none of which would now be employed.

I switched on my kindle, clicked the magnifying glass symbol and entered one word.

'Capybaras'.

"This reminds me of when we travelled in the nineties," I said to Fiona at breakfast the next morning. "Here we are, surrounded by travellers in their twenties who speak various languages, all chatting to each other and fostering international relationships."

The dining area contained eight tables with a provisions counter against the rear wall. I breathed in through my nose and inhaled the smell of freshly ground coffee.

Fiona massaged her head. "I wish they'd chatter more quietly. I shouldn't have had that second schnapps glühwein."

Candi placed a plate on the table containing four enormous pieces of toast buried one inch thick in chocolate-coloured goo.

"Are you sure you've enough spread there?" My eyes goggled.

She grinned. "This place has all-you-can-eat Nutella. I'm going back for more after these."

"What about the orangutans?" Ellie pressed her lips together and glanced downward. "The trees grown to harvest palm oil for Nutella deprive them of their natural habitat."

Candi crunched her toast. "I'd better eat as much as possible, then, before it becomes illegal."

"I wish they had fruit," said Fiona. "I'm hanging out for fresh food. All we eat in Europe is sausages and bread."

"And Nutella," said Candi, beginning her third piece.

I rubbed Fiona's shoulder. "I promise we'll eat fresh food today. You've been to France before; you know what French cuisine's like. There'll be loads of vegetables to go with steak."

"And we'll be in the Alsace," she said. "I hope my hangover's gone so I can enjoy a good Gewürztraminer."

I raised my mug. "Have another coffee. Despite coming from a machine, it's pretty good."

"Why not practice your French?" I asked the girls. "Could you ask for the towel deposit refund?"

"Can I keep the money?" asked Candi.

"Did you pay in the first place?"

"No."

"Guess not."

"I'll ask," said Ellie. "I want to make the most of being in French-speaking countries for the next couple of days." She approached reception, returned and handed me twelve euros. "Easy. They understood me perfectly. It's so weird, using words with native French-speakers we've learnt in class. It's hard to believe this experience is real."

Candi polished off her fourth piece of toast. "The Nutella's real enough."

"This," announced Fiona, "is like taking a tour through the best bottle shop you could ever visit."

We'd elected to drive on the scenic route and follow the Moselle River towards our destination in the Alsace region of France. The road bordered the river precisely and shared every twist and turn. Steep slopes rose perpendicularly on the opposite bank, and dormant rows of vines attached to wires marched up the hills.

"I thought we were in France," said Ellie. "Why do these towns have German-sounding names?"

"Aha," I said. "The Alsace is an enigma, an area which can't decide whether it's French or German. Most of its residents, known as Alsatians…"

"Is this area inhabited by dogs?" asked Candi.

"…which is pronounced the same way as the dog breed, speak French, although they're also fluent in the Germanic Alsatian dialect and refuse to use standard German, despite being perfectly capable of understanding it."

"So, are we in France or Germany?" asked Ellie. "That sign advertised a wine called Niersteiner, which sounds German."

"The Alsace currently resides in France, although it produces Germanic-sounding beers such as Kronenbourg, and Germanic-sounding wines such as Mum's favourite Gewürztraminer."

"Look," said Ellie. She pointed across the river. "There's someone working on the crop."

We stopped to watch an elderly man perched on a trolley attached to a pulley system. It transported him and his supplies up and down the precipitous slopes as he tended the vines.

"Could we stop at a vineyard and have a tasting?" asked Fiona.

"I haven't seen anywhere open. Let's continue to Kaysersberg. We'll have to stop at some point. We need petrol."

"Turn right," instructed Kylie, and she led us across a small bridge to the opposite side of the river. The road became rougher and more uneven, and it narrowed. More men and women attached to pulleys worked vines halfway up the slopes, and we heard their shouts to each other as they executed tasks the same way they had for generations.

"Is this definitely the right way?" asked Fiona, as she braced herself against bumps in the road. "This is making me car-sick."

"I'm following Kylie's directions. She hasn't let us down yet."

"What about the field up a mountain in the middle of nowhere in Luxembourg?" asked Candi.

"My fault. Not Kylie's. I gave her the wrong instructions."

"I'm all for taking the scenic route," said Fiona, "but this doesn't look right at all."

We pulled over as a construction truck thundered past, a plume of ochre dust billowing from its rear. Around the next corner, we passed three men working with a digger and shovels, moving a large, yellow pile of earth. They waved as we passed.

"The locals are friendly, aren't they?" I said, as I swerved around the edge of the dirt mound. I waved back and continued.

"I'm not sure they were waving," said Candi. "I think this road's being repaired. It's closed."

"It can't be. We didn't see any signs. Plus, Kylie would know and divert us."

We continued bumping along the gravel track, the river always to our left. Grapevines marched up every hillside, and we slowed several times to take photos of the scenery.

"Dad," said Ellie. She pointed through the windscreen. "There are barriers ahead. I'm not sure we can drive much further."

46

"Nonsense." I pointed at the Google Maps display. "This shows we join another road in one hundred metres."

"We don't, Dad. Stop! The road's blocked."

6. NATIVITY

Orange-and-white-chevronned signs barricaded our route, and another pile of saffron-yellow earth buried the road surface. Our tyres skidded as I slammed the brakes on, and my chest sproinged against my seatbelt.

"How did we come this far?" I asked. "There weren't any 'road closed' signs."

"Maybe we missed them?" said Fiona.

"Turn left," said Kylie, far too enthusiastically.

Ellie slumped in her seat. "We'll have to retrace our steps all the way back to the bridge. Another hour of holiday wasted."

A yellow petrol pump symbol glowed at me from the dashboard.

"I'm not sure we'll make it if we turn around," I said. "We'll have to push through."

"What d'you mean?" asked Fiona. "The road's blocked. We should've stopped when those road workers waved."

"It's easy. We move the sign and edge the car past this mound of sand. No problem."

"You can't relocate road signs, Dad," said Candi. "It's illegal."

"Yes, I can. There's no-one watching." I opened the car door and glanced left and right to make sure there wasn't.

On the other side of the obstruction, the gravel track we'd negotiated joined up with a perfectly good road leading into a village. Dust blew from the top of the sand heap, and I rubbed my eyes.

"Whoops," I said, as I lifted the sign, slid it aside and jumped back into the driver's seat. "It moved by itself."

"We're not in a four-wheel-drive," said Fiona.

The Peugeot leant at an angle and dug into the pile of sand. Candi opened her window and snapped pictures.

Fiona gripped the handle above the door. "I hope you haven't invalidated our insurance," she said, as the wheels returned to the horizontal and plopped back onto the road.

I applied the handbrake and moved the sign back to its important job of preventing less-disobedient drivers from doing what I'd done.

"Turn left," repeated Kylie.

"Where is everybody?" I asked, as we entered the village and pulled into a small petrol station featuring one elderly, rusty pump.

The wind blew dead leaves around the forecourt. A loose-fitting door leading to a shed at the back rattled.

"Everyone's hiding," said Candi.

I pulled my collar up and wiggled the door's handle.

Locked.

"Dad," shouted Ellie. "It's ten past twelve."

"So? Is it illegal to buy petrol in the afternoon or something?"

"It's lunchtime. Lunchtime in rural France. You've no hope of buying anything until after two. Everything in France stops for lunch."

"Oh, yes." I flopped into the driver's seat. "We'll have to wait."

"We can't sit here doing nothing until two," said Fiona. "How far is it to Kaysersberg?"

"Um, fifty kilometres?"

"Let's hope the car has a big reserve tank."

"Make a U-turn where possible," advised Kylie, as I restarted the car.

We meandered through the stark, winter beauty of the Alsace; desolate, frost-covered fields interspersed with occasional church spires which betrayed the location of tiny hamlets. I crossed my fingers and prayed we wouldn't be stranded by the side of the road, fuel-less, and more worryingly, lunch-less.

"Simon, petrol station. And it's open." Fiona gesticulated wildly to where a big, beautiful sign announced 'Essence sans Plomb (Unleaded Petrol)'.

The car stalled, restarted and stalled again. Momentum carried us to a stop in front of pump one.

"Bloody hell, that was close." I exhaled loudly. "Well spotted. Pass me the Visa card."

Despite the lunch hour, several customers filled tanks and trooped in and out of the shop with purchases. I relaxed at the familiarity of petrol station etiquette, helped by the globally identical scent of unleaded fuel.

My French language skills wouldn't be any use here. The pump showed a symbol of a non-gender-specific person's head and shoulders, a euro currency sign and an outline of a hand gripping a nozzle. In what I hoped was international procedure, I unclipped the hose, inserted the end into the car's petrol-filling hole, pulled the trigger and waited.

Nothing.

I glanced at the shop, but the attendant paid me no attention. His conversation with a customer involved extravagant actions not unlike those a primary school child would enact to accompany a boisterous nursery rhyme.

Now what?

I clicked the nozzle back into the holster, raised my eyes at the shop again and unclipped it once more.

Still nothing.

'Heads and Shoulders, Knees and Toes' continued on both sides of the counter.

Fiona leant out of the car window. "Maybe you pay in advance?"

I replaced the nozzle again and strode into the shop, where the action song had completed, and the attendant stood with an unlit Gauloises cigarette stuffed under an opulent moustache. He gazed out to the forecourt and beeped buttons on his till. A faint smell of engine oil permeated from an open door behind him.

"Excusez-moi, monsieur (Excuse me, sir)," I said. "Je ne peux pas, um, prendre l'essence de la pompe (I can't take the petrol from the pump)." Clearly, my attempt to explain I couldn't make the pump work labelled me as an English-speaking idiot, incapable of following simple, pictorial instructions.

"Zat is pompe one. Eet ees for ze people who live 'ere. You must 'ave ze special card." He brandished a black plastic rectangle at me, which I concluded was a membership scheme for French-speaking non-idiots.

He pointed. "Number trois." He held up three fingers in case I'd failed to understand his Franglais. As I had demonstrated an excellent level of oral French, I couldn't understand why he didn't converse with me in his native language.

"Pump three. Right."

"Pump one," I explained to my family, as I ploomped back into the seat, "is for members of some local scheme. We need to drive to pump number three on the opposite side."

I pressed the start button.

Nothing.

I pressed it again.

Still nothing.

"Why won't the bloody car start?"

"We ran out of petrol?" suggested Candi.

"Oh, yes. Everyone out. We'll have to push it over there."

"You can't push an automatic," said Fiona.

I slapped my forehead. "Great. Now what do we do?"

"See if they have a petrol container you can borrow. Fill it from pump number three and pour it in the car, so you can start the engine. Then drive to pump number three and top up the tank."

"This is all becoming very complicated." I blinked rapidly and opened the car door again. A short queue of a Renault 4 van and a little tractor had formed behind me, clearly comprising members of the local petrol club who didn't appreciate their personal pump being blocked by stupid foreigners. I ran into the petrol station.

"Oui?" said the attendant, who thankfully had failed to light his Gauloises.

I'd forgotten the French word for 'borrow', so I substituted the one for 'hire'. "Puis-je louer un, er, bidon d'essence (May I rent a petrol container)?"

The attendant chuckled, reached under the counter and produced a red canister covered with oil stain-coloured fingerprints. "C'est gratuit (it's free)."

The tractor driver gesticulated at me as I performed my complicated dance around the forecourt.

"I'm not sure you've made a great impression on the locals," said Fiona, as we exited the petrol station. "That farmer gave you a very, um, French expression."

"I'm starving," said Candi.

"Six pieces of Nutella toast should keep you going for the whole day," said Ellie.

"We'll be in Kaysersberg soon." I accelerated around a corner. "We'll stop for lunch. I'm hoping we find a restaurant to taste the local cuisine."

Fiona licked her lips. "And a bottle of local Gewürztraminer."

Kaysersberg had two immediately obvious qualities: a beautiful, medieval town centre and scant parking. As in many well-touristed locations, the residents suffered the dual-edged sword of income from visitors' money and absolutely nowhere to keep their own vehicles. The sound of stationary car engines queuing to compete for spaces as they became vacant contrasted with slamming doors and human voices whenever a team of contestants championed. We eventually squeezed into a space a significant distance from the town centre. Potentially convenient for another town entirely.

"It's freezing," said Fiona, as a light dusting of snow fell. A low, stone wall bordered the footpath, and I heard rushing water on the other side. Pink and orange-coloured houses guarded the opposite bank of the stream, and we crossed a bridge barely wide enough for a vehicle.

I pulled my jacket around my face. "Let's pile into the first decent-looking restaurant we find and warm up over lunch."

"This place looks full," said Fiona, as she swept her eyes around a low-ceilinged restaurant crammed with French-speakers eating, drinking, conversing, laughing. Black-waistcoated waiters sashayed between the groups. I inhaled the scent of home cooking and heard a cork being removed from a wine bottle.

"Don't worry," I said. "I'll talk them into finding us a table."

"Good afternoon, sir." An elderly man with deep folds in his face greeted us. His enormous nose betrayed a productive wine-tasting career. "'Ave you a reservation?"

How does he know we're English speakers before I've opened my mouth?

"Um, no. But we've travelled all the way from Australia, as we've heard about your famous cooking, and it would devastate us if our journey had been in vain."

That should do it.

Fiona rolled her eyes while the gentleman shrugged with his entire body and arms. He flagged down a waiter and spoke in heavily accented Alsatian French, a dialect I struggled to understand. We followed the server through diners' conversations and plates steaming with the scent of home-cooked goodies to a table for four. He handed us each an eight-page menu, and we slid out chairs.

"This is pleasant," I said, as he departed. I unwrapped my scarf. "See, my flattery worked."

"Yes, Simon." Fiona patted me. "We'd starve to death without you." She slipped off her coat and hung it on the back of a chair.

I tuned into conversations on adjacent tables, and I could tell they spoke French, but the speed of the discussion caused the words and meaning to elude me.

"Girls," I said to my daughters. "Remember to practise your French with the waiter."

Ellie smirked. "What, like you did with the maître d'?"

"I'm sure you'll do better."

Candi opened the menu and stretched her neck as the waiter attended to the next table. "What are they having?" she whispered.

I glanced at a lady who'd been presented with a meal which extended beyond the boundaries of her plate. "It seems to be a pork knuckle."

"I'll have one of those."

"It's enormous, Candi. You'll never finish it."

"Watch me."

The menu thankfully listed offerings in both French and English.

"What would you like, Ellie?" I asked. "The local dish in this region is tarte flambée. This establishment serves twenty different flavours. Which d'you fancy?"

"Is it the Alsace equivalent of pizza?" asked Ellie, gazing at more dishes laid in front of the neighbouring table. "The same base with different toppings?"

"Yes. Tarte flambée's made from dough rolled out into a circle, like pizza. Then it's covered in sloppy, cheesy sauce and topped with ham and onions. Although, like the evolution of the pizza from a simple Italian snack to a fast-food meal served in cardboard boxes throughout the western world, restaurants have expanded the tarte flambée menu to the point where you can order almost anything."

"I didn't ask for an entire food travel guide, Dad."

"The important thing is," I said, rubbing my hands together, "we're eating local cuisine. I mean, you can't pop into Domino's Pizza in Melbourne and ask for a"—I ran my finger down the menu—"tarte flambée foie gras, can you? Or even a pizza foie gras."

Ellie poked out her bottom lip. "I'm not eating foie gras. It's cruel to the geese."

"I reckon everywhere in Alsace sells foie gras; another dish this area's famous for."

"The thought of foie gras sickens me. I'll have the flambée végétarienne."

Candi poked her. "But then you're being cruel to the broccoli."

I rubbed my hands together. "One pork knuckle and one flambée végétarienne. Fiona?"

"They have Gewürztraminer on the wine list," she said, showing me the menu. "Five different types."

"I meant which tarte flambée?"

"Oh, sorry. I haven't perused the food yet."

"Flambée champignon for me," I said. "Mushrooms. Yum. I bet they're locally picked."

"Salmon, please," said Fiona. "It'll go perfectly with Gewürztraminer."

A waiter brushed crumbs from a neighbouring table, sat four people at it and swivelled to face us.

"Hello. May I take your order, please?"

"Puis-je avoir le porc? (May I have the pork?)" asked Candi.

"Ah, you speak French?"

"Oui," said Candi.

"Very good," said the waiter. "One pork." He glanced at the kitchen. "Ze last one, I think."

I wished he'd converse with her in French, instead of neither party speaking their native language and having this odd conversation where we're speaking French and the French people are responding in English.

"Et pour moi, flambée végétarienne," said Ellie.

"Ah, you speak French too?" The waiter opened his eyes wide and smiled.

"Oui," said Ellie.

"I am sorry. We do not have the flambée végétarienne. It is two o'clock."

I opened my eyes wide. "Is it illegal to eat vegetables at two o'clock or something?"

The waiter frowned and tilted his head. "Non. We 'ave none left. Lunch is finish. We also 'ave none of flambée champignon, flambée saumon, flambée foie gras, flambée carpaccio or flambée trois fromages."

"Um, what do you have?"

"Flambée nature and flambée gratinée. That is eet."

"Do you have Gewürztraminer?" asked Fiona.

We wandered the cobbled streets, replete from local tarte flambée and local Gewürztraminer. The timbered buildings stood higgledy-piggledy, decorated with religious Christmas decorations like a set from the *Beauty and the Beast* movie. An entire life-size nativity stood under the town cross surrounding a realistic baby Jesus. Hundreds of tourists strolled with us, admiring the multi-coloured houses and purchasing knick-knacks from the shops bordering the narrow streets.

Fiona hugged herself. "I am absolutely bloody freezing. I desperately need to buy a thicker coat and a fluffier hat. This place is pretty, but I need to return to the car right now."

I squeezed her. "I think we've seen it all, anyway. Let's continue to Colmar. It's not far."

I'd love to say our decision to stay in the ridiculously attractive Alsace town of Colmar was based on an appreciation of its historical architecture, or a desire to experience its unique, perfectly preserved, medieval centre.

In fact, we'd elected to visit entirely because of Fiona's favourite television program.

7. ICE SKATING

Years previously, Fiona had become glued to a lifestyle documentary series called *Escape to the Château*, in which a talented engineer named Dick Strawbridge and his multi-colour-haired wife, Angel, bought a gigantic, tumbledown gazillion-bedroom French castle for next-to-no euros, intending to renovate it, possibly not for next-to-no euros. Dick Strawbridge spent happy days single-handedly improving the castle from the top down and inventing complicated machinery from old ironmongery excavated in the grounds, while Angel's pastimes suggested she was a frustrated *Blue Peter* presenter, as Lesley Judd-like, she produced intrinsic, shiny artworks made from little more than old magazine cuttings, string and glue.

During one memorable episode the year before our trip, this couple had driven the entire girth of France to unearth goodies for their forthcoming Christmas celebration. They'd arrived in the attractive town of Colmar, a place we'd never heard of, and Fiona had called me from the living room to watch them.

"Simon, quick. On the TV. Quick! Come now."

I'd rushed out of my study, imagining some terrible natural disaster was playing out on the screen, and the news would show a major city flattened to rubble.

"*Escape to the Château*." She jabbed her finger at the telly. "They're in Colmar."

I rolled my eyes. "Lovely. Looks attractive."

"Isn't that where we're going?"

"We are?"

"We pass Colmar between Luxembourg and Switzerland. Could we stop there for a night?"

So, to emulate Fiona's sticky-back-plastic heroes, we did.

The parking space associated with our apartment lay in a tiny, gated alleyway five millimetres wider than our Peugeot.

"This is nuts," I said, leaning out of the driver's window, as Fiona and the girls stood outside and watched me perform a 763-point turn. "It's not as if we're in central Paris. Why is the space so small?"

"Colmar's an old town, with narrow streets," explained Fiona. "We were lucky to find an apartment with a parking space at all. Let's unpack, throw on our warmest clothes and explore."

"And buy dinner?" asked Candi.

"Far out," said Fiona. "Where d'you put it all? We'll buy groceries and prepare them in the apartment tonight."

"Local groceries?" asked Ellie. "We have to eat local food, remember?"

We dumped our bags in our top-floor apartment, clothed ourselves in every layer we owned against the cold, dank air that clung to each surface and marched out to investigate the town.

The town centre came to life after dark; people thronged everywhere, music played from multiple directions simultaneously and every street was stacked full of brightly lit stalls selling traditional market food, drink and knick-knacks. A larger version of Kaysersberg, Colmar's colourful, half-timbered buildings in its immaculately preserved medieval centre displayed a vast assortment of Christmas decorations and coloured lights. Old-fashioned Dickensian streetlamps lit the pavements. Every building was floodlit in pink, blue, orange, green; every tree had been draped in white bulbs. Its primary economy today consists almost entirely of tourism, and I was glad we were visiting in winter as, in summer, the streets must've been impassable.

"These shops resemble a Christmas movie." Fiona gazed in every window with her mouth open.

"Yep," I said. "All it needs is snow, and we could be in *The Grinch*. No chance of a dusting tonight; I can see stars above."

Every turning, every side alley exposed a new vista of a new market, with more and more jubilant people laughing, drinking and eating. Cinnamon and clove smells assaulted our nostrils, and our feet scrunched on salt scattered across the pedestrianised streets.

"The Europeans know how to enjoy themselves in winter, don't they?" said Fiona. "In Australia during the cold season everyone hides indoors after dark and watches TV."

"Let's go out next winter. Let's pretend to be European, not hide indoors and watch TV. I'll bet you complain about the cold."

"It's different here. Everybody's partying. In Australia, it'd be us wandering the empty streets."

"This whole place is one gigantic Christmas decoration," said Ellie. "Um, could we have some vin chaud now?"

"Vin chaud?" I asked. "Hot wine?"

"It's what the French call glühwein. I think I prefer the German expression."

We warmed up with a vin chaud each and entered a large grocery shop.

The scene reminded me of Harrods' food hall on a busy Saturday morning. Glass-fronted counters contained encyclopedias of cheeses, cold meats and pastries. Elongated salami hung from ceiling hooks like a conjuror's balloon animals. Rows of wicker baskets flaunted seasonal, green vegetables. I rubbed my hands together and sniffed in the wonderful smells of French rural ingredients as, surrounded by Alsatians performing their daily shopping, we stood, unsure where to start.

"What's the local delicacy here?" asked Candi. "Apart from flambéed tarts or whatever they're called."

Fiona pointed at a circular pastry with a slice chopped from it. "It's Quiche Lorraine."

"Quiche Lorraine?" I snorted. "That's not a local delicacy. My mum used to make it from her *Good Housekeeping* recipe book. It's an English picnic staple."

"It is Alsatian," said Fiona. "This is where it originates from."

"Gosh, my mother's cooking was more international than I gave her credit for."

We selected a suitably local Quiche Lorraine, a French baguette, because, as Ellie said, you can't have a meal in France without a baguette, some Camembert cheese and a chicken terrine. As we headed back through the crowded streets, the girls heard dance music pumping.

Candi tugged Ellie violently. "Come on. It's kicking off over there."

They ran on, and Fiona took my arm.

"They're loving Europe, aren't they?"

"Yep. It's wonderful to see their faces light up with all the new experiences. People said we were silly to come to Europe in winter, but I reckon it's the best time."

Fiona gazed around the streets. "I wasn't expecting all these Christmas markets. I mean, I knew about them, but didn't realise the scale of them. I think Colmar's the best so far."

"Mmm. Wait until we reach Munich. I reckon that'll be bigger and better."

She squeezed my hand. "And Switzerland. I can't wait to see Switzerland again."

"And after all the Christmas markets, the capybara in England." I grinned and hugged an imaginary cuddly animal.

"You and your capybara." Fiona prodded me.

"Did I tell you; I bought a new book for my kindle? *Capybaras: A Complete Owner's Guide.*"

Fiona's eyes opened wide, and she let go of my hand. "Simon, I'm happy for you to visit that zoo in Bristol and have an up-close-and-personal capybara experience. I'm not happy for you to bring one home." She marched off, and I ran after her.

We found the girls bouncing up and down inside a large tent, surrounded by French people consuming vast quantities of vin chaud. Most of them failed to retain the wine in their glasses as they pogoed. A plump, middle-aged, bearded DJ dressed in a red puffa waistcoat and a Santa hat presided over the celebration.

"Here we go," he shouted in English, accompanying a song I was more used to being sung by a Liverpool Football crowd. "Here we go, here we go. Everybody, jump, jump, jump." The song changed to one with a single repeated word as its lyric, as dancers flung more and more wine around the tent and small children jerked on parents' shoulders until I thought they might throw up. The grins on my girls' faces as they snapped pictures and shared them with their friends in Australia stretched wider than The Joker's.

"I love Colmar," said Ellie, as they rejoined us for the walk home. "I wish we weren't leaving tomorrow."

I woke, reached up and tugged the curtain. "Oh, wow," I shouted. I grinned and bounced on my heels. "Girls, get up. Quick. Look out of the window."

Scrambling and thuds echoed from the next room.

"Has it snowed again, Dad?" called Ellie's voice.

"Nope. But you won't see this sight at home."

Colmar lay shrouded in fog. Fog so thick you could plunge your arm into it and lose your fingers. The blurry blobs of streetlights glowed through in regimented rows, but we couldn't see the other side of the street. I felt a tingle of excitement run from head to toe as the scene transported me back to childhood winter's days, when weather closed schools, and children rejoiced, cast aside study books and tugged sledges from sheds.

"Woah," said Candi. "I have to take a photo. Where's my phone?"

"The fog's so soft and fluffy," said Ellie. "Like a big, grey marshmallow."

Fiona stood next to me in her pyjamas. "Could you buy breakfast and bring it back?" Her fingers rubbed a hole in the condensation. "I'm not sure I want to step outside. It looks so cold."

"I think we should all choose something from the French bakery," I said. "We'll be in Switzerland later today, then Liechtenstein, Austria and Munich. No more French food."

Ellie's shoulders slumped. "Back to stodge-land."

Wrapped in coats, hats, scarves and gloves, we ventured out into the cumulonimbus which had elected to enjoy a pre-dawn rest on Colmar's boulevards. Somehow, the cloud made things sound quieter, more muffled, though we knew this didn't agree with the laws of physics.

As we left the safety of the apartment and entered the cobbled streets, we discovered something else we weren't used to in Australia.

"Shit!" said Fiona, as she slipped and grabbed at me. "Ice. The whole town's a skating rink. Why haven't they salted the pavements?"

My cheeks stung with the freezing temperatures, and I clasped a pole and stepped forward gingerly. "It must be too early. It's 7:30 a.m."

Ellie and Candi shuffled, slid and held on to railings. A lady ahead of us completed an entire pirouette with her wheeled trolley before snatching awkwardly at a stop sign. I planted my feet slowly and wondered how these uneven, cobbled streets could've turned into such a uniform, perfect sheet of ice overnight.

The girls became braver and enacted Torvill and Dean-like performances, before Candi crashed into an estate agent's shop front.

Ellie giggled and pointed at her.

"Stop laughing," said Candi, rubbing her nose. "That hurt."

"I wish I'd videoed it," said her sister, holding her stomach. "It'd go viral."

"Seriously, girls," I said. "Please be careful. We have travel insurance, but it'd ruin our holiday if anyone needed a hospital."

Fiona and I slid hesitantly along the edge of the street, grabbing at everything which didn't move. Signposts, railings, shop door handles, parked cars, they all became supports for our slow progression.

We arrived at the town square and congregated in the gloom.

"We must plan our route across carefully," I said. "The last thing we need on this holiday is a broken hip."

"Where's the bakery, Dad?" asked Candi.

I indicated a street leading from the square's opposite side. "Over there. We need to cross two streets to reach it, and it'll be a miracle if we all survive upright.

We traversed the first street. At one point I felt myself falling and floundered my arms in the air like one of Magnus Pyke's more enthusiastic demonstrations. As we edged along patchy ice under shopfront eaves, we came face-to-face with another group of people headed in the opposite direction.

The question was: Who had the right of way? A silent negotiation began as we faced off and eyed each other.

Their footwear seemed more suited to the conditions.

We were tourists; they were clearly locals.

They were older than us.

62

Who had the advantage? Who, ethically, should sacrifice themselves to release their one-handed hold on the shop front and allow the other party to proceed safely?

I prepared to boom Gandalf-like, "You shall not pass," when Fiona tugged me around them, and I gripped the shop again on the other side.

At the second road crossing, we stood on the pavement and gazed at our prize. The lights of Paul Le Boulanger shone from across the street, and we viewed the rows of croissants, pains au chocolat and other goodies with rumbling stomachs.

As we hesitated, a young Frenchman approached and grabbed Fiona.

8. GINGERBREAD MEN

Fiona pulled her arm back, but the young Frenchman held her tightly.

"Madame, puis-je vous aider? (Madam, may I help you?)"

A cigarette stuck out of his mouth between his dark, closely cropped beard, and he wore a long, smart, grey coat.

Before anyone could object, he'd looked left and right, then helped her across the road as if she were significantly more elderly than a fit lady in her forties. We had no choice but to follow gingerly as he marched her skillfully to the opposite pavement.

Fiona's cheeks glowed the colour of a stoplight, possibly not from the cold.

"Thank you," called Fiona after their brief encounter. The young man waved one hand and vanished into the mist.

"What a gentleman," said Fiona. "What an absolute gentleman. The French are so well-mannered. And he was very good looking."

"Was he?" I said. "I didn't notice. It's a shame he smoked."

"All the French smoke," said Ellie.

We unlatched the bakery door, and the unique essence of French bread wrapped us in its comforting, motherly bosom.

"I can't believe how cheap it is," said Ellie. Her gaze darted from shelf to shelf of the brightly lit counter. "You can buy a croissant for one euro, twenty cents. That's two Australian dollars, right, Dad?"

"Yep." I picked up a free sample of fresh bread from the top of the counter, popped it in my mouth and experienced the light, fluffy, melt-in-your-mouth texture. "Bread's such a staple of French culture and cuisine that every village has a bakery, and the bakers have a roster so they don't all go on holiday at the same time."

"We learnt that in French," said Candi. "There's a law in France that baguettes must be baked using only flour, water, yeast and salt. No additives or preservatives."

"So, the bread lasts less than a day before becoming stale, preserving the centuries-old French tradition of everybody visiting the bakery each morning."

Ellie continued inspecting the prices. "In the bakery at home where I work, croissants are six dollars. And pains au chocolate are one euro thirty here. They're seven dollars in Australia. I wish we could fill a suitcase and take it home."

"We could fill a suitcase and not take it home?" suggested Candi.

"Or we could buy enough for breakfast," said Fiona. "Four of each will be more than sufficient."

"Oui?" asked the shop assistant. Her short, plump stature levelled her nose roughly with the countertop, so unless we stood on tiptoe, we could only see the peak of her white hat.

I pushed Candi to the front and hissed, "This is your chance to practice French."

Candi turned and looked at me. I prodded her and whispered, "Four croissants and four pains au chocolate."

The assistant looked at her expectantly. "Oui?" she repeated.

"Quatre croissants, s'il vous plaît, et quatre pains au chocolat." Candi turned to me and beamed.

The lady tonged them into a bag.

"Voudriez vous quelque-chose d'autre? (Would you like something else?)"

I smiled and patted Candi's shoulder as the assistant continued the conversation in her native language.

"What are those things resembling giant gingerbread men?" Candi asked me. "How do you say, 'gingerbread man' in French?"

"Not sure. Hommes de pain épice (men of spicy bread)?"

Candi pointed at the gingerbread men. "Deux, um, hommes de pain épice, s'il vous plaît."

"Deux mannalas?" said the lady, waving her tongs at them.

"Oui."

"Douze euros quatre-vingt (twelve euros, eighty)." The bakery assistant bagged our goodies, and I fished out change.

We returned to the skating rink, our journey made more challenging by our yummy-smelling paper bags which restricted free hands available for panicked arm-flaying and random object-grabbing.

"Are we driving to Switzerland after breakfast?" asked Ellie. "Gosh, it sounds weird saying that; in Australia, we'd fly over three hours to reach another country."

"Yes," I said. "It's two hours to Biel 'slash' Bienne."

"What is there to do in Biel/Bienne?" asked Candi. She broke pieces from her croissant, as Fiona placed a coffee on the table. "And why does it have two names with a 'slash' in the middle? Are those its pronouns?"

I wafted the commingled smell of fresh coffee and fresh bread towards me and regretted booking only one night in Colmar. "Some parts of Switzerland speak French, and some parts speak German. Biel/Bienne's on the border of both parts, so it has a French name and a German name. And some parts of Switzerland speak Italian too, and there's an old Swiss language. Plus, you'll find almost everyone speaks English."

"It's hard enough learning French," said Candi. "I'm glad I don't go to school in Switzerland and study all those other languages as well."

"The cloud's lifted." I gazed from the apartment window and watched daily Colmar life play out below, as umbrella-wielding pedestrians dodged past each other on the narrow pavements.

"It still looks cold. But we must check out by ten, so we don't have long. We haven't packed yet, and Candi's room resembles an explosion in a Kmart warehouse."

Fiona tested a Mannala's left arm. "Why don't we phone the landlord and ask if we can leave the car here after we've checked out?"

This was the first phone call I'd made on my new SIM, which, though issued by a Spanish telecom, the vendor had assured me worked in every European country.

I pushed buttons on my phone and listened to the dial tone, followed by a rapid announcement from a Julio Iglesias-soundalike.

"I don't think it's working," I said. I dialled again and heard the same message.

"It's a Spanish SIM, right, Dad?" said Candi.

"Yep."

"We're in France."

"I know. The person I'm dialling is also in France."

"Try adding the country code for France."

"Why? You don't when dialling France to France."

"Maybe you do when you're dialling through Spain? That's why you're hearing a Spanish recording."

"Oh. What's the country code for France?"

"Three-three," said Fiona.

I tried again. Gérard Depardieu replaced Julio Iglesias, and another one of those odd conversations ensued where I attempted to speak French to a native French speaker and the native French speaker responded in English.

"What d'you want to see in Colmar this morning?" I asked Fiona, once car parking negotiations had concluded. "We won't beat last night's experience, and the markets will be closed now."

"There's an area called Little Venice which is supposed to be pretty, with canals."

"Ppff," I said. "They'll be frozen."

"And we need a shop, or a market, for lunch."

"Great," said Ellie. "Picnic in the car again. We always have car picnics."

"We ate in a restaurant yesterday," I reminded her. "Have you forgotten tarte flambée?"

"Could we eat at a restaurant for lunch today?" asked Candi.

Fiona ignored them and continued with the morning's itinerary.

"And on our way to Switzerland, we'll visit New York."

I frowned and tilted my head. "Did they name everything in this town after foreign cities? Venice, New York? Is there a part of Colmar called London?"

"I'm going to show you something which'll surprise you," said Fiona, mysteriously.

Workers had scattered salt across the icy pavements by the time we reached the location of our earlier skating rink. The narrow streets glistened in shop lights, which brightened the gloomy day. Colmar's half-timbered, colourful buildings would appear attractive in any season, and the weather didn't dampen our spirits.

"Mum, the clothes shops are open," said Candi.

"What are we waiting for, girls? In we go."

"There's no time for shopping," I said, looking at my watch. "We need to be in Switzerland this afternoon."

My words reflected off the glass shop door swinging closed in front of me. I knew better than to enter the shop with them, so I stood outside and studied the architecture.

Maybe all of France had resembled this once. I'd seen nothing similar in Paris, or Lille, or Le Mans. The five-storey buildings crowded together, leaving a cobbled street in the centre wide enough for a car or horse and cart to pass. Every window displayed exterior shutters, painted in contrasting colours to the dwellings they swung from. Some buildings were buff-brown, some creamy white, some yellow, some pastel greens and blues. Plain, wooden, half-timbered, centuries-old decoration surrounded attic windows.

With my shoulders back, I stared at the unfamiliar construction and laughed silently to myself as I imagined being a character in an episode of *Blackadder*.

My family arrived.

"Did you find anything?" I asked, narrowing my eyes at their empty arms.

"No," said Fiona. "Just looking. Ooh. Across the street."

The three of them dashed to another shop, which sold the same items as the one they'd vacated, and I continued my architectural inspection.

Colmar's nods to the modern age comprised the electric lights beaming from the shop windows, an occasional television aerial, and green, plastic wheelie bins. Everything else dated from the era of the town's construction. The buildings stood in uneven rows, like illustrations in a children's nursery rhyme book.

I swivelled on my heels, stepped forward and ran my hand over the rough, uneven stone, then glanced over my shoulder as I realised I was rubbing the front of a local resident's home.

My family exited the shop and permitted us to continue our stroll to Little Venice.

"Dad," said Candi. "Take my photo." She handed me her phone and nipped up a side street so narrow, she could touch both side walls with the tips of her fingers.

A channel ran along the centre of the cobbles.

"D'you know," I said, "in the olden days people would go to the toilet in a bucket, and throw the contents out of the upstairs window, where it would run down this groove in the middle of the street and end up in the canal."

"Seriously?" Candi glanced up at an open window and scarpered from the alleyway. "That's disgusting. It can't be legal. It must be against French hygiene regulations."

I laughed. "They don't do it now. I'm sure these houses have had flush toilets for years."

"I can see why this part's called Little Venice," said Fiona, as we pushed our way through throngs of people and attempted to gain a glimpse of the canals. "There are as many tourists here as there are in the real Venice."

"We're part of the problem, aren't we?" asked Ellie.

Fiona shrugged. "But did everybody have to come here at the same time as us?"

"Come on, Ellie," said Candi. "Let's snap pictures for our stories."

Fiona and I found a gap in the multitude and leant over a railing. We stared at the mirror-still, mist-shrouded water surrounding the bases of the colourful buildings and the disused, winter-stored boats tied against their edges, covered with tarpaulins white with frost.

"It does resemble Venice, doesn't it? Although I'm considerably colder here." She squeezed up to me, and I recoiled as she placed her chilled hand on my cheek to demonstrate this.

"D'you remember our weekend in Venice?" she said, smiling and fluttering her eyelashes. "It must be twenty years ago now. So romantic."

"The one where we couldn't find our accommodation and nearly ended up sleeping on the street?"

"Um, yes. Is that the main thing you remember? Not our gondola ride or sitting in a cafe in St Mark's Square? Shall we take a selfie?"

"Okay." I lifted my phone. "Come this side of me. Where are you? Why aren't you in the picture?"

"Don't cover the lovely, colourful houses with our faces."

CLICK

"Take another one. I think I blinked."

CLICK

"It's a good job we can snap unlimited pictures these days. Imagine if we still had thirty-six to a film?"

Fiona nudged me as I scanned the glass displays in the indoor market, replete with local produce. "You're not buying any smelly cheeses. When you eat smelly cheese, everything else tastes like smelly cheese."

I drank in the display of wedges and circles with labels announcing interesting-looking fromage varieties I'd never heard of and determined one mission in the few French hours remaining to me.

Before we returned to the sausage-world of Germanic cuisine, I would eat a bloody good Roquefort, and no-one would stop me.

The only cheese the European Union Appellation d'Origine Contrôlée regulations permit to be labelled Roquefort must be aged in the town caves of Roquefort-sur-Soulzon. The mould that gives the distinctive taste and smell is found solely in the local soil. Being expensive and hard to find in Australia, whenever visiting any country where the French had a gastronomic influence, I stocked up with as much as I could politely consume.

As Ellie was the one other member of my family who appreciated its finer qualities, little competition existed for any I purchased. The downside (or upside, depending upon your point of view) was the smell. Those who appreciate Roquefort waft their hands towards their noses at the unwrapping of a freshly cut wedge, as Michel Roux might demonstrate to a sous-chef in the kitchen of Le Gavroche.

Unfortunately, Fiona was not a member of the Roquefort fan club.

9. MUSIC

"Deux cent grammes de Roquefort, s'il vous plaît (Two hundred grammes of Roquefort, please)," I said to the lady behind the counter. She picked up a lump of blue-veined, creamy wonderfulness and placed it in a cheese slicer.

"Isn't Roquefort a smelly one?" asked Candi.

I glanced over my shoulder. "I don't, um, notice any particularly strong fragrance."

"You can't fool me," said Fiona. "You can stand outside the car and eat it."

The lady performing the slicing operation paused, inhaled deeply through her nose, and smiled. I hoped Fiona hadn't noticed this gesture, and my stomach rumbled as I watched her wrap my little parcel of joy in white, waxed paper.

"Could we buy some Brie, please, Dad?" asked Ellie.

"Of course. You can order it. Practice your French. What would you like, Fiona?"

"Do they have Cheddar?"

I laughed. "We're in France, not England. The hard cheeses are at this end."

Fiona selected a suitably Cheddary cheese, and the lady wrapped it. We added a baguette and some marinated olives and headed back to the car.

We found the Peugeot squashed in where I'd left it the previous night, sandwiched in the alley between high brick walls and other residents' vehicles. I pulled my jacket around me. Although my watch read 12:00 noon, the temperature remained below zero and the cold penetrated my clothes.

"I've no idea how I'll manoeuvre out of here." I slid and grabbed hold of a neighbouring Renault's door handle. "The car's crammed into a tiny space, and the ground's so slippery."

"We've a bigger problem," said Candi. "It's covered in a sheet of ice."

Having been brought up in England, I was accustomed to scraping ice from windscreens on winter mornings.

This was on another level.

Our car was, as Candi had observed, buried in a thick sheet of ice. The windows, the bonnet, the doors, the boot. The only part which didn't shine from a translucent shroud was the tyres.

I cracked my knuckles. "Ha. You all laughed at me when I said I'd brought an ice scraper. You won't be laughing now." I rummaged in my hand luggage and produced the promised implement which had only ever been used to defrost a chest freezer.

My chipping and scraping efforts created shavings, then I lost my balance and fell between the cars.

One of my hands grazed on the concrete, and the other turned red from contact with the ice, as I supported myself on a wing mirror and tugged my body upright. I held my knee and wiped my hands on my coat.

"You said we won't be laughing now," said Candi, snapping a photo of me. "I am."

"It's not funny," I said, clenching my teeth. "You try."

"It's more fun watching you."

I discovered by repeated experiment, if I slid the edge of the scraper under the ice sheet on a car body panel, a square metre of frozen water would detach from the vehicle and shatter on the ground. I competed against myself to slice off ever larger sheets.

"Make it quick," said Fiona, hugging herself. "I'm freezing."

"I'm taking care not to fall over again. How will we drive to Switzerland if I break a leg?"

After I'd surrounded the car with more smashed ice than in Selfridge's fish display, I hopped in the driver's seat, lowered the window and instructed my family.

"Candi, make sure I don't scrape the wall. Ellie, please fold in that wing mirror so I don't clip it. Fiona, could you watch the other side?"

Fiona pointed to her chattering teeth. "Hurry. I'm so cold."

I leant out of the window. "I can't hurry. If I scratch the car, our insurance excess is three thousand euros."

The car inched towards the exit gate. I felt it slip sideways, and braced myself against the wheel, as if the action would prevent this.

"Fiona, open the gate," I shouted. "I daren't brake; I'll slide into it."

"How?"

"Push the green button."

"It's not working."

"Push it harder."

Fiona frantically jabbed at the button to open the high, metal gate before I generated a large repair bill, and it creaked open slowly. In a well-timed action, Fiona dropped the apartment keys in the letterbox, and my family lunged into their seats.

"Time to visit New York," Fiona announced. "Set Google Maps for the Statue of Liberty."

"The Statue of Liberty? It'll say, 'can't compute route'."

"Ask it to find the Statue of Liberty, Colmar."

I gave her an odd look. "Okay, Kylie. Drive to Statue of Liberty, Colmar."

"Dad," said Candi. "Kylie doesn't know she's called Kylie. Say 'Okay, Google'."

"Okay, Google. Drive to Statue of Liberty, Colmar."

"Turn right," said Kylie, confidently.

I followed her directions, and we departed the town along a wide avenue.

Fiona pointed. "There. See?"

Although we approached from the rear, the unmistakable outline of the Statue of Liberty materialised through the misty rain, holding her torch high in the air, as my father had seen her when he disembarked from the Queen Mary on arrival in New York in 1948. I opened my eyes wide and gazed upwards as the windscreen wipers swish-swished across my view.

"It's a one-quarter-size replica," explained Fiona, "erected in 2004 to mark the hundredth anniversary of the death of Frédéric Bartholdi, her designer. He came from Colmar."

"It's a shame they situated her on a traffic island," I said, as we paused at the entrance to the roundabout.

"Quick." Candi unlocked her phone. "Ellie, take my picture with the statue behind me. People will think I'm in New York."

We circumnavigated Liberty and headed down the opposite carriageway.

"I'm hungry," said Candi.

"Me, too," said Ellie.

I glanced ahead at a turning. "Let's park in this industrial estate and have some lunch."

"Beautiful location for it," said Candi.

"Enough of the sarcasm. If you want to eat somewhere beautiful, we'll drive further to Switzerland, where we can eat our bread and cheese in the foothills of an Alp. Not for two hours, and you're hungry now, right?"

"It is one o'clock."

"Right," I said, applying the handbrake outside a warehouse. "This'll do. There's no-one around."

We retrieved the bread, cheese and olives and balanced them on the centre armrest.

A van parked beside us. Through the rain sluicing down our windows, I observed a man climb from the driver's seat. He wore a long coat and ducked as he entered the warehouse. I watched his back disappear through the opening, tilted my head and frowned.

"It's lucky I brought a knife," said Fiona, as she sawed at the baguette.

Another car pulled up, and a second man with his overcoat lapels upturned slammed the driver's door and nipped into the building.

I eyed Fiona's knife. "Could I borrow that to cut my cheese, please?" I unwrapped the waxed paper around my Roquefort.

"Simon, leave the car. You are not eating your cheese in here. It stinks."

"But it's raining."

"I don't care if it's snowing. Eat it outside."

"I like Roquefort too," said Ellie. "I'll come outside with you, Dad."

The long-coated man exited the door in front of us, carrying a parcel wrapped in plain brown paper.

"This doesn't make sense," I said. "Two of us enjoy Roquefort, and two of us don't. Why do we have to eat outside? Why can't you two stand in the rain?"

"The whole car smells of it now, anyway," said Fiona. "It's too late. But you're not touching it with my knife."

Fortunately, the Roquefort's consistency allowed us to cut and spread it with the butt end of a spoon. We sat and munched our bread, olives and assorted cheeses. Flakes of breadcrumbs covered our laps, the seats and the armrest.

Fiona opened her door. "I'll brush all the bread out of the car before we depart." She stepped out, as the man with upturned lapels exited the warehouse and leered at her strangely.

Fiona twisted around to inspect the location we'd chosen for our picnic, then poked her head into the car. "Simon, did you realise we'd parked outside a sex shop?"

"The Swiss mountains'll make the ranges in Australia look like molehills." I grinned as we headed south towards the border. "They're even taller than the Southern Alps in New Zealand."

"Will they have snow on them?" asked Ellie. "Or has global warming melted it all?"

"There'll be tons of snow. Tons and tons. All the way down to the foothills. Your Insta-chats will be filled with stunning photos. What else d'you know about Switzerland, apart from the fact it has mountains and snow?"

"They make chocolate," said Candi. "Can we buy some?"

"Of course. Shops in Switzerland have entire sections dedicated to chocolate. Fiona, d'you remember when we came here at Easter? The whole floor of a department store with different-sized Easter bunnies?"

"Yum," said Candi. "But it's not Easter. It's Christmas. There won't be bunnies."

"There'll be Lindt," said Fiona, rubbing her hands together. "And Toblerones. Flavours we don't see anywhere else. I love Lindt. I could eat a ball after every meal."

"Christmas," said Ellie. "I keep forgetting. It doesn't seem real, in the cold."

"How ironic," I said. "People brought up in the Northern Hemisphere wouldn't feel Christmassy in the heat."

"Let's play Christmas music to put us in the mood," said Fiona. "Pass me your phone."

To the accompaniment of assorted screechings by Mariah Carey, we crossed the border and entered the girls' country number twenty.

Our Swiss accommodation stood beside a lake, behind rows of sailboats tarpaulined for the winter. A trailer with a rack of ten canoes partly covered in ice stood parked against a wall. Lines of small, metal rowing boats lay upside down, chained together.

"This is creepy," said Ellie. She stepped from the car slowly, gazed around and blinked rapidly. "Abandoned. Like a scene from a dystopian post-apocalyptic novel."

I heard children's voices and gazed across the car park. "Look. Those kids are playing football in the snow."

We turned to watch. The boys shouted, while running and shoving each other. In time-honoured, international, park-soccer fashion, two scrumpled jumpers at each end of the frost-dusted field formed the goal posts.

"They're shouting in French and German," said Candi. "I can understand some of what they're saying, but it's a weird combination. It doesn't sound right."

The difference in temperature as we entered the hostel made us tear off our coats immediately. A long bar overlooked a high-ceilinged dining room containing square tables and chairs and, at the end, a hatch formed the reception desk. No customers or staff occupied the area.

I attempted to ring the small, circular bell to announce our arrival, but a huge, affectionate tabby cat blocked my way. He stood on the chest-high counter, pushed against my hand and refused to let me check in.

"Here's the security guard," I said.

"He's so cute," said Ellie. She stroked the cat, who smooched around her and purred like a malfunctioning pneumatic drill. "What's his name?"

"No idea. I can ring for attention, now you've distracted him."

I dinged the service bell, and a young, bearded man entered from a back room.

His reaction was instantaneous. He swung open the door through which we'd entered, extended his left arm and shouted, "Aus, aus! Get out!"

10. CHAMPAGNE

We froze and glanced at each other. Being evicted before we'd checked in was an unexpected experience even for our family.

"Not you," said the receptionist. "The cat." He plucked the large tom from Ellie's embrace and ejected it into the cold. "Oliver must stay outside. If he comes in, he eats the other cat's food." He pointed to the floor behind us, where a pair of small, metal bowls lay empty. Two eyes peeked from under a chair.

Ellie crouched down and peered back at them.

"She is twenty years old," said the man, "and she is blind."

Ellie tried to entice the elderly cat, but she wouldn't come.

"Good evening," I said, hoping we'd now dealt with the feline items on the agenda. "Prior family, checking in."

"Hello. You have number twelve; an upstairs family room with its own bathroom." He dangled a key. "Breakfast is eight euros each, served from seven until nine."

He handed us four towels which felt thin and scratchy.

"At least we don't have to rent towels here," whispered Ellie.

Candi tapped her phone. "What's the wifi password, please?"

"Take a picture of it," suggested the receptionist, and he held up a laminated piece of paper which said 'W-LAN password: gW*3)DKl3@p!65?'

"Um, thanks," said Candi. "I hope I don't make any spelling mistakes."

My family dragged bags out while I held the door and stuck out my leg to prevent the big tom from re-entering.

"Let Oliver in," said Ellie, conspiratorially.

"We're not allowed to," said Candi. "What about the old cat?"

"I know," said Ellie, "but he'll be cold in the snow. Please, could we take him to our room, Dad? I want to pat him. Just like you want to pat that capybara."

"That's different. The capybara's outdoors."

"Please, Dad?"

"No." I clenched my jaw. "No way. I will not have a strange cat climbing over our bags and leaving hairs on my bed. And that's final."

We clanged our bags up the metal fire escape to the first floor and opened the door to room twelve. One double and two twin beds filled the room, with minimal space to walk between them. A slight musty smell wafted towards us, and a metallic banging noise sounded like a crew of miniature miners were trying to escape from the heating pipes.

"D'you think anyone else is staying in this place?" asked Fiona. She darted a glance each way along the walkway. "It's eerie."

"Someone's in the shadows," said Candi. "I smelt their cigarette." She chose one of the two single beds and dumped her bag, then entered the complicated wifi password and began scrolling through her phone.

Ellie stared out of the window into the dark. A light snow fell, and the flakes fluttered under a streetlamp illuminating the car park. She rotated back towards the room and warmed her backside on the heater. "What is there to do in Biel 'slash' Bienne?"

"It's not really a tourist town," I said.

"So why are we staying here?"

"This accommodation suited us, as it was reasonably priced and convenient for more exciting Swiss locations, like Bern and Interlaken. We'll drive to those tomorrow."

Ellie frowned. "Are we going to do anything this evening? Or am I stuck in here watching Candi post photos of herself on Snapchat?"

"I," called Fiona's voice, "have an exciting activity planned for us." She emerged from the bathroom and zipped up her trousers. "What's Switzerland most famous for?"

"Chocolate," said Candi.

"Mountains," said Ellie.

"The World Wide Web," I answered.

Candi frowned. "Isn't that American?"

"Nope. The Internet started in America, but an Englishman called Tim Berners-Lee working at CERN in Geneva invented the World Wide Web."

Fiona nodded. "All of those, but also: watches. This town's where the Omega factory's located. There's a Swatch museum too. We could visit and pick up dinner from a supermarket."

"That sounds boring," said Candi.

"D'you have any other suggestions?" I asked. "We need to venture out to buy food, anyway. You never know; you might enjoy it."

We drove through the softly falling snow, to the repeating squawking of Mariah Carey's Christmas album, which Fiona failed to substitute.

Among a gloomy, industrial townscape, characterised by wide streets jammed with traffic, the Omega and Swatch factory stood out as a modern facility on a small hill at the edge of town. Its exterior architecture reminded us of a gigantic noughts-and-crosses board, and its high ceilings swept across the cathedral-like reception area.

We were the sole visitors on this wet, cold, midwinter's evening, and I imagined the staff had hoped to pack up early and head home. The lift brought us to the second floor, and we stepped out and gasped.

So many Swatches.

Designer Swatches. Plain Swatches. Art déco Swatches. Mundane Swatches.

Huge Swatches. New Swatches. Old Swatches. Blue Swatches.

Production-line Swatches. Limited-edition Swatches. Handmade Swatches. One-off Swatches.

"I never imagined this company made so many designs," I said to Fiona, within earshot of an employee. "Swatches were popular in the eighties; I haven't seen them recently."

The museum guide swept her arm around the exhibits. "This is less than half of the collection. We don't have enough room to display them all. There is the Omega Museum downstairs too."

I discovered a machine where I could take my picture with various backgrounds and spent a happy ten minutes dragging my family into it to pose for photos. We then inserted ourselves into a circular chamber and watched a 3D video about the history of time.

As the movie room doors opened, I stepped out and found myself face-to-face with James Bond.

"Daniel Craig wore Omega," said Fiona. "Isn't he gorgeous?"

I studied the model of him in full naval attire, as Fiona trailed a finger along the sleeve of his jacket.

"D'you like a man in a sailor's uniform?" I asked her. "You don't call me gorgeous when I'm wearing my Coast Guard outfit."

"You're not James Bond, are you?"

I was in the process of inspecting an exhibit depicting the 1969 lunar landing, and wondering whether Fiona felt the same way about men in space suits, when an announcement sounded in German, French and English.

"Guten Abend. Bonsoir. Good evening. The museum is closing. Please leave by the main exit. Thank you for visiting."

As there weren't any more men in uniform to ogle, we obeyed the instructions.

"Okay Google," I said, as we fastened our seatbelts. "Nearest supermarket."

Silence.

Candi and Ellie scrolled through photos and chattered.

"Ssh, everyone. I need Kylie to hear me."

"Okay Google," I repeated, "Nearest supermarket."

Nothing.

I inspected the phone. "The bloody SIM's not working again. This is rubbish. It's supposed to connect everywhere in Europe."

"Have you tried turning it off and turning it on again?" suggested Fiona.

"I'm sure that's a line from *The IT Crowd*. Okay, I'll see if it helps."

The phone rebooted, but with the same result. No connection.

"How will we find our way home?" asked Fiona.

The windscreen wipers swished-swished automatically. I peered into the dark streets.

"I have Snap Maps," said Candi.

"We drove around Mainz for two hours because of Snap Maps. I'm not repeating that experience."

"I remember the way home," said Ellie. "All we need to do is retrace our route in reverse. Not in reverse. Backward. You know what I mean."

"Okay. You sit in the front and tell me directions." Ellie swapped seats with Fiona.

"At the end of the road, turn right," said Ellie-nav, efficiently.

I laughed. "Have you taken lessons from Kylie?"

Ellie led us to the town centre, where I briefly parked illegally while my family found an Aldi supermarket. I sat alone in the car, fiddled with the phone and steamed a few angry words to direct at the company which had sold me this so-called European SIM, guaranteed to function in every European country.

Thanks to Ellie's navigating, we rediscovered the hostel, where Oliver greeted us at our door.

Ellie bent down to stroke him.

"Please, can we let him in? It's so cold out here." She smiled as he rubbed his head against her. "I'm happy to share my dinner with him."

"I don't think he'll eat pasta."

"You could give him some chicken, Dad?"

"I am not giving that gigantic fat cat my chicken. Bloody hell. Shoo! Go find someone else to beg from."

Ellie furrowed her brow at me. "You're mean, Dad. Poor Oliver. I'll bet you'd let him in if he was a capybara."

We closed the door and left him curled up on the mat.

Before bed, I composed an email to the SIM company, which I hoped conveyed my current mood.

>>URGENT: SIM NOT WORKING

I purchased a so-called European SIM from you, which stated it was compatible with every European country. We have arrived in Switzerland, and although it worked briefly, it no longer connects to any mobile network. I checked the settings you gave me, and they are correct. Please help urgently. We are driving around Europe and rely on it for navigation.

I pressed 'send', shut the laptop's lid, climbed into bed and opened my kindle. "Did you know, everybody," I announced, as I started chapter three, "capybaras can hold their breath for up to five minutes? They can even sleep underwater."

Fiona turned over. "That might be more comfortable than this bed."

1:30 a.m.

I was in the middle of a dream where I found myself attending a high-society party with Fiona, although for some reason I cuddled an enormous tabby cat under one arm. Daniel Craig approached, holding a Champagne bottle and two empty flutes. He brushed me aside, raised his eyebrows at my wife and passed her a glass. While she fluttered her lashes at him and smiled, he forced the cork from the bottle with a skillful, practised motion.

POP

I opened my eyes.

Outside our room, voices shouted and laughed. Daniel Craig evaporated in a puff of sophistication.

I propped myself up on my elbows and glanced towards the door.

"What's that noise, Dad?" asked a voice from Candi's bed.

"People outside being too loud, too late. Bloody inconsiderate. Hopefully, they'll shut up."

I lay my head on the pillow and tried to return to sleep.

The partying continued. Another cork-popping noise echoed through our bedroom door, followed by the clink of glasses and an exclamation.

"This is most unreasonable." I slipped out of bed in my pyjamas and opened the door. A wall of cold air slapped my face, and a low mist drifted in front of the car park's street lamp. The walkway which ran past the first-floor rooms contained several young people engaged in an impromptu party. I assumed they were fellow guests.

"Gute nacht (good night)," I said. "Bitte nicht so laut. Es ist spät. (Not so loud, please. It's late)."

They continued with their celebrations as if I were invisible.

I raised my voice. "Can you be quiet, please? It is very late."

One of them looked at me, grinned and said, "We will try."

I closed the door and returned to bed.

The party continued.

"Dad," said Ellie's voice. "I can't sleep."

"I know. I'll have another word."

I opened the door again, and the revellers were once again treated to the sight of my pyjamas. "Can you shut up, please?" I made a zipping motion across my lips. "Kein sprechen (no speaking). It is almost two o'clock."

I slammed the door dramatically and returned inside again.

"They're speaking French, Dad," said Ellie. "You told them off in German and English."

"Whatever. They'll understand my intention."

"They don't," said Candi. "They're still noisy."

"What else can I do?"

I wrapped my pillow around my head and slept fitfully, interrupted by singing, popping corks and one smashed bottle.

Until 6:00 a.m, when a noise penetrated my eardrums as if a rhino had stepped on a set of bagpipes.

11. LIGHTS

MIAOW

My hair stood on end as I lifted my head up from the pillow. "What the hell's that?"

MIAAAOOOOW

"It's Oliver, outside our door," said Ellie. "He must be hungry. I'll give him the leftover tuna."
"You will not." I sat up. "If you feed him, he'll never leave us alone."

MIAOOOOOOOWWWW

"I've had about five hours' sleep. Shut up, cat."
Sorrowful mews and miaows emanated from under the door.
"Anyone would think that animal had never been fed. I'm taking a shower. And don't let it in while my back's turned."

SIM support hadn't responded to my email.
"Bloody hell," I fumed. "No response from what's laughably called 'support'. How will we find our way around Switzerland? I'm not suffering hours driving around in circles like in Mainz."

86

"No," said Fiona. "My stomach feels sick thinking about it."

"You could see if their website has a chat function?" suggested Candi.

"Chat function?"

"Yep. These companies have an instant chat box on their websites where AI responds to frequently asked questions."

"AI?"

"Artificial Intelligence."

"Oh, great. All I want to do is find my way around Switzerland, see the Alps and eat some Lindt chocolate, and now I feel like a character in *Terminator 2: Judgment Day*."

"Try it, Dad."

The website did indeed have a button: 'chat with us'. I clicked it.

>>>Hello, I'm Sima. What can I help you with today?

"She looks professional in the picture," I said to Candi. "She's wearing a smart business suit."

"Dad, she's an avatar."

"Oh, right. More movies."

>>> Hello, Sima. I bought a SIM from your company which was supposed to work throughout Europe. I'm now in Switzerland and it doesn't connect. Please help. Thank you for your assistance. Regards, Simon.

Candi rolled her eyes. "Dad, you don't have to sign it like a letter. You could've put 'SIM not work Switzerland'. It would've been the same to the AI."

"She's called Sima, Candi. Not 'The AI'."

"Whatever."

I grinned. "Sima says she's typing. Here we go."

>>> I'd be delighted to help you with that, Simon. Let me study my knowledge base and I'll be right back to you.

"She's polite."

"Sure, Dad."

"Ooh. She's typing again. She must be able to fix it." I held my breath.

>>> Hello, Simon. I've found an answer to your question. SIMs sold by our company do not work in Switzerland. Is there anything else I can help you with today?

"Help? What does she mean, help? She's been no help at all." I threw my hands up, then typed again.

>>> When I bought the SIM, you assured me it worked in every European country.

I turned to my daughter. "There, Candi. I didn't sign it this time."

>>> For a full list of countries, please visit the product page on our website. Is there anything else I can help you with today?

I puffed. "Sima's not very helpful, is she?"

"Do what she suggests, Dad. Visit the product page."

I clicked 'products'.

"Which SIM package did you buy?" asked Candi.

"This one." I pointed. "The one lasting thirty days which works in every European country."

Candi ran her finger down the screen. "Switzerland isn't in the list of countries."

"What d'you mean, Switzerland isn't in the list of countries? It's in Europe."

I scrolled up and down and verified there were no entries listed alphabetically between Sweden and the United Kingdom.

"Bloody hell." I slammed the laptop lid. "How are we going to find our way around today and tomorrow?"

"Maybe the hostel has a map we could use?" suggested Fiona.

"A map," I said. "How quaint."

I opened the door and tripped over Oliver lying sheepdog-like across the entrance.

"A map?" asked the receptionist. "SIM problems?"

I tilted my head. "Yes, how did you know?"

"It's the same for everyone. Switzerland's the only country where European SIMs don't work. Swiss SIMs work here. Nothing else."

"Oh. I didn't realise."

"I have a map; it is basic. Where are you driving?"

"We thought we'd go to Bern, then Interlaken."

"Easy." He scrawled on the outline map. "Turn right out of the hostel to the centre of town and follow the signs for highway six to Bern. The same road goes to Interlaken. It's one road there, and one road back."

"Thanks; that sounds simple enough. We'll look for route six."

"I love all these white trees," said Ellie. "I feel like shaking them to knock all the snow off."

Stuffy, warm air pervaded the car as I lost the continual battle with Fiona to select a temperature amenable to both of us. "This is remarkably straightforward," I said, as we zipped along the black, four-lane highway bordered by snowy fields and woods. "It's like the old days. Who needs Google Maps or Snap Maps?"

"Us," said Candi. "When it's time to return to the hostel."

"We're going to waste an entire day driving around in circles again, aren't we?" said Ellie.

"We'll be fine. You kids have never experienced the joys of heading along a motorway, your partner sitting in the front seat twisting a multi-folded road map upside down, asking where we are right now, then you both yelling at each other 'cos the turning you were supposed to take is now behind you."

"Sounds idyllic," said Candi.

"I hope that behaviour doesn't happen today," said Fiona.

"Where are all these stunning mountains you keep talking about, Dad?" asked Candi. "All we've seen is cloud."

Fiona glanced out of the passenger window. "Hopefully it lifts later. The Alps take your breath away."

I grinned as I drove and tapped the steering wheel. "Someone else has had her breath taken away now we've no SIM, thank goodness."

"What d'you mean?" asked Fiona.

"No more Mariah bloody Carey. No SIM; no music."

"Aww. I like Mariah. Let's put the radio on." She scrolled through the car's display.

"How far is it to Bern?" asked Candi.

"We're almost there," I said, as Fiona discovered a radio station that played non-stop Christmas hits.

"What? We've only been driving for half an hour."

"Yep. Cities are closer in Europe than in Australia. We exit the motorway here." I indicated and swung the wheel right. "Now we need to look for city centre signposts. We're in German-speaking Switzerland now, so they'll say 'Zentrum'."

Fiona pointed. "There. Zentrum. Parkplatz. Does that mean car park?"

"It does." I nipped down a side turning, followed a 'P' sign and stopped next to a ticket barrier. "We've made it. See, girls." I lowered the driver's window and extracted a car parking ticket. "It is possible to navigate without technology."

"What are we doing here?" asked Candi, as we poked through an alleyway into the main street and faced the giant clock tower at the end. I flinched, as a tram rattled past crowded with passengers dressed in the homogeneous European winter uniform of black coats and grey scarves.

"Seeing the sights; soaking up Switzerland."

"Soaking's right." Ellie stuffed her hands in her pockets and stared at the pavement. "It's snowing. Rainy snow."

"Let's visit Einstein's house," said Fiona. "He lived here for part of his life, and his house is a museum."

"The father of modern physics." Ellie nodded. "We learnt about him at school. $E=mc^2$."

"Yep. What else did you learn about him?" I asked.

"Not much."

"Excellent. You can learn more today and tell your friends about it when you go home."

"Dad, we're on holiday," said Candi. "This isn't a school excursion."

We climbed steep steps to a first-floor room above a shop. A loud grandfather clock tick-tocked slowly, as we approached a thin, elderly lady behind a mahogany desk that may well have belonged to Einstein himself.

"Guten Tag (Good day)," she said. "Vier Leute? (Four people)"

"Yes, please. Two adults and two students."

"Twenty-four francs, please."

I offered her my Visa card.

She inspected it as if this was the first time she'd encountered such a 21st century item. "Cash only."

I furrowed my brow. "Really?"

"Ja. The ATM is across the street." She pointed a bony finger towards the window.

We traipsed back down the stairs.

"I'm amazed," I said. "The Swiss have the reputation of being the world's bankers, yet they won't accept a credit card."

"You'd think if Einstein was so clever," suggested Candi, "he would've installed a card reader."

Once we'd agreed on a suitably old-fashioned method of payment, we entered the tiny, two-roomed museum. A lace-covered table stood in the centre, surrounded by four wooden chairs with red-patterned seat cushions, and a rug of a similar design lay under it.

"He married his cousin?" asked Ellie, as she read from a display. "Is that legal?"

"Yes, and not only in Switzerland," said Candi. "Under the current law of Australia, it's legal to marry your cousin. You could lawfully marry Josh."

"Yuck. No, I couldn't."

"Marrying your cousin was common in those days," said Fiona.

Ellie glanced around the small room. "Einstein didn't have much space. I wonder where he performed all his experiments?"

"In his mind," I said. "Everything was theory."

"E=mc² wasn't real?"

"Who knows? No-one's been able to travel at light speed to test it."

"And," said Candi, reading from a description, "he was unqualified at the time he made his most important discoveries."

Fiona puffed. "That doesn't mean you can slack off studying for your exams."

Einstein's house took around twenty minutes to examine in minute detail, and we soon found ourselves on the pavement again.

"What else is there to do in Bern?" asked Candi.

"Let's walk down the street and see if we can find a Christmas Market," suggested Fiona. "I could do with a glühwein to warm me up. Maybe see how Swiss markets compare to French and German ones?"

We strolled away from Einstein's house towards the town's main square. On a sleety, foggy winter's day, outdoor attractions had limited appeal.

"Christmas Market alert," shouted Ellie, and we turned right into the customary area filled with row upon row of wooden stalls and anticipated the steam of warming hot drinks.

"Where's the glühwein?" asked Fiona. She peered down one of the alleyways.

"And the sausages," said Candi. Her mouth pressed into a grimace.

"This is all clothes and trinkets," I said. "It's not a patch on the markets in Germany or France. Or Luxembourg."

"We need a market leaderboard," said Ellie. "And right now, Switzerland's at the bottom. Colmar's on top, Mainz is second and Luxembourg's third. I wonder if there'll be Christmas markets in Liechtenstein and Austria?"

"Don't forget Munich," I said. "That'll be number one on your ladder, I'm sure."

We swept out of Bern on the main road. My finger tapped on the steering wheel while Fiona scanned through the radio stations trying to find one free of static.

"Forty-five minutes to Interlaken," I announced. "This route six is easy."

"Yep," said Candi. "You and Mum haven't killed each other yet or held a map upside down. Amazing."

"Look," said Fiona. "The cloud's lifting."

Through the tops of the clouds, a tiny portion of blue sky materialised, and the snowy peak of an alp punctured it. The clouds merged again, and it disappeared.

"Did you see?" I asked the rear seat occupants. "Mountains."

"Where?" said Candi.

Fiona pointed. "If you took your eyes off your phone, you'd see a lot more."

"I didn't see them either," said Ellie. "All I can see is cloud."

"You'll have to take our word for it. Switzerland has the most amazing mountains."

"I see them," said Candi.

92

Ellie swivelled her head from side to side. "Where?"

"On my phone. I'm following hashtag Switzerland. Dad's right. They look incredible."

I frowned. "How are you connected to wifi?"

"I've tethered to something called Henrik's iPhone. He must be in the car in front."

By the time we reached Interlaken, the cloud lifted, and we parked the Peugeot beside an enormous field in the centre of the town, surrounded by tall peaks with snow-dusted trees cascading down their slopes.

I stepped out of the driver's door, grinned and swept my arms around the scene. "See, girls. Mountains. Loads of them. Welcome to Switzerland. This is what I wanted you to experience."

We watched as a series of parachutists oscillated like dead autumn leaves falling from a tree and landed on the field behind us with varying degrees of competence.

"Let's find lunch," said Candi. "We haven't been to a Swiss restaurant yet. We have to eat the local cooking to count this as a country."

"Um, the Swiss aren't known for their cuisine," I said. I rocked my head from side to side. "I'll tell you what. We'll eat in the hostel restaurant tonight. Then you'll taste local food."

"Can we take some for Oliver?" asked Ellie.

"Oliver?"

"The cat."

"No, we bloody can't." I shook my head. "He looks like he eats enough."

"So, what are we having for lunch?" asked Candi.

"Um, supermarket picnic?"

"Could we buy some Swiss chocolate?"

"Of course. That's one food the Swiss are known for."

In the supermarket, ranges of packeted snacks filled the shelves. Despite Ellie's protestations about single use plastic, we each chose something.

We also bought multiple bars of chocolate from racks of selections, each decorated with photographs of snowy mountains, sanitised cows, or green, flower-strewn meadows. Some displayed all three.

"Dad," said Candi, as we left the supermarket, "there's a phone shop across the road. Maybe you could buy a Swiss SIM?"

"Great idea. Maybe you could buy one too?"

"I don't need one. I'm picking up free wifi from the Tourist Information office."

93

I swung open the door of the Swisscom shop. Scattered pedestals each featured a single phone displayed on top, and bright-red brochures announced various special offers in German. I could tell they were special offers, as, helpfully, the phrase 'special offer' had been written in English. Two shop assistants conversed at the rear of the showroom, and I hesitated before approaching them.

"Gutentag," said one of them; a young, bearded man. "Kann ich ihnen helfen? (May I help you?)."

"Gutentag. Ich möchte eine SIM kaufen. (I want to buy a SIM)."

"Ah. English. Hello. How long do you need the SIM for?"

"Two days."

"Our minimum is one week. It is twenty euros."

I wanted to say 'shut up and take my money', but though the assistant spoke excellent English, this might be a colloquialism too far.

"Yes, please. That'll be perfect." I pulled my Visa card from my wallet while the assistant removed a SIM from his drawer.

"This is great." I gave Fiona a thumbs-up. "There's no chance of becoming lost again."

"And," she said, "we can have music."

"I just remembered. Swiss SIMs don't play music. They don't play Mariah Carey, anyway."

"Very funny." Fiona nudged me.

The assistant rang up twenty euros on the till, and I handed him the credit card.

"Thank you, Sir. Please, could I see your passport?"

"My passport?" I shrugged.

"Yes, Sir. It is not permitted for a foreign person to buy a SIM in Switzerland without a passport."

"Ah. I don't have mine with me." I turned to my family. "Has anyone brought their passports?"

"No. You told us to leave them in the hostel safe."

I turned back to the assistant. "I have my driving licence, if it helps?"

"Sorry, Sir. Passport only."

I replaced my credit card in my wallet and resigned myself to never being able to use a mobile phone in Switzerland.

"This salad tastes of nothing but cabbage," complained Ellie, as we sat on a bench and ate our purchases.

The winter sun shone on the backs of our necks. I'd failed to find the lake, so we dined by the kerb of the main thoroughfare, where passers-by inspected our lunch. We answered their inquiring looks with stares and frowns, which didn't dissuade them.

"Yep, this pasta doesn't taste of anything." Fiona replaced the lid on her container.

I chewed. "My sandwich is floppy, like it was made yesterday. Why don't the Swiss take a leaf out of their neighbour's book and learn cookery from the French?"

"This chocolate's pretty good," said Candi. "I'm still deciding whether I prefer Lindt or this cheaper variety."

"Is that all you're having for lunch?" I asked. "Chocolate?"

"Judging by the comments about your own lunches, I made the right decision."

"Let's explore the shops and leave," said Fiona. "It'll be dark mid-afternoon, and we must find the road home."

"It's easy. Highway six takes us all the way."

"You sound confident."

"I am."

Traffic whizzed past us in the pitch black. BMWs, Mercedes and Audis all travelled at velocities far speedier than cars on Australian roads.

"Slow down," said Fiona.

I lifted my foot off the accelerator. "Why? Everyone's overtaking me."

"I can't believe how fast they drive here," said Ellie. "And it's snowing. How would they stop if there was a traffic jam?"

"The European drivers are used to these speeds," I said. "Statistically, European roads are far safer than Australian highways."

Ellie glanced out of the window at cars' tail lights disappearing into the distance. "They don't feel safer."

I slammed on the brakes, as a red glow clustered directly in front of us.

"See," said Ellie. "There's an accident ahead."

"It might be evening commuter traffic."

"Look." Fiona pointed. "The cars in both lanes are splitting up, pulling over to each side. You should as well."

"I wonder why they're doing that?"

As I bumped onto the right verge, blue and red lights flashed in my rear-view mirror.

"It must be the law here, to leave a clear path in the middle for emergency vehicles," said Candi. "Everyone seems to know the rule, and they obey it. Good idea. We should do it in Australia."

The ambulance flashed beside us, and we heard the Doppler effect of its siren as it passed. A second ambulance followed minutes later.

"I wonder if anyone cheats and nips down the middle after the ambulance?" asked Ellie.

"Yep," I said. "Here comes some idiot."

A large BMW bisected the queues.

"Maybe it's a doctor?"

"Maybe, but they should have flashing lights. I reckon it's someone who thinks they're above the law."

We crawled on. A police car flew down the newly created centre lane, followed by a breakdown truck.

"I wonder how far ahead the accident is," I said. "I hope they haven't closed the road. If we're diverted off highway six, we're stuffed. We'll never find our way to Biel/Bienne."

"See, Dad," said Candi. "You do need technology."

Fiona craned her neck. "I see something in the distance."

Twenty minutes of crawling later, a line of traffic cones and a police officer with a glow stick guided us around an upside-down vehicle. The damage was so extensive, we couldn't recognise what model car had been wrecked. Another policeman swept broken glass while, two hundred metres ahead, the breakdown truck loaded a second, less-damaged vehicle. The ambulances had gone, and our tyres scrunched on debris as we edged past the accident. Ellie stared at the carnage illuminated by blue, red and white flashing lights and covered her mouth. "You were saying European roads are safer, Dad? A few minutes earlier and that could've been us."

The traffic returned to its pre-crash speed as soon as we left the accident scene behind.

"They're crazy," she said. "Everyone's driving as if the crash never happened. We'll probably see another one."

Thankfully, Ellie's prediction didn't come true, nor, amazingly, did we get lost. Lights from the hostel restaurant windows shone out as we parked under the streetlamp.

"We made it," I said. "Everyone ready for traditional Swiss food?"

"Sure," said Candi. "The cold and the snow make me hungry."

Ellie poked her. "You don't need cold and snow to make you hungry."

We pushed open the reception door. Blaze from a fire flickered in the corner of the dining room, and I unzipped my jacket. A young girl wearing jeans and a black T-shirt carried meals to chattering diners.

We stood in front of the blackboard menu and inspected the offerings.

Fiona puffed upwards. "This is a café in a hostel, but the prices resemble a Michelin-starred restaurant."

"Yep. Switzerland can be expensive."

"I wonder what the costs are in Liechtenstein. Hopefully cheaper."

The waitress paused, her hands full of dirty dishes. "Guten Abend."

"Guten Abend. Wir übernachten im Hostel, und wir wollen essen (Good evening. We are staying in the hostel, and we'd like to eat)."

"No problem. You are English?"

"Australian, actually."

She turned and shouted towards the kitchen. "Shaun. Come out here. Some of your mates have turned up."

12. FIRE

A tall, young man with a beard and tousled hair popped out of the kitchen, wiped his hands on a cloth and held out one hand. "G'day guys, are you Aussies?"

"Yep, we're from Melbourne. How ya going?" I had a brief realisation of how easy it was to slip back into the Australian vernacular after conversing in assorted combinations of European languages.

"Good, mate. I'm from Brisbane. How long are you here for?"

"Two nights. We're headed to Liechtenstein, Austria and Munich."

"Liechtenstein, hey? Not many people visit there. I hope you don't blink and miss it."

"Me, too. How long have you lived here?"

"Six years. My mother's Swiss, and most of my family's here. I prefer it to Brisbane. It's a nicer lifestyle."

I considered the traffic on the dark, snowy, motorway versus the golden sands and turquoise seas of Queensland and mulled over how subjective lifestyle could be.

"Anyway," he said, "I'd better return to the kitchen. Sorry guys, the last fillet steak went out."

"All good. I'm not sure we can afford fillet steak."

"Maybe try the raclette? A Swiss speciality."

"I've had raclette," Fiona whispered to me. "It's nothing special. Melted cheese. We could make it at home."

I rubbed my chin and inspected the menu. "Um, I don't think we can afford the raclette, either."

"If you're on a budget," continued the chef, "the soup's good tonight. Made from my own traditional Swiss recipe."

"D'you feel like soup, Fiona?"

"If it's traditional Swiss, sure."

Our cobbled-together meal ended up comprising the cheapest items on the menu: soup, chips, and one portion of chicken wings shared between us. Alcohol was well beyond our financial ability, and we sat at the table with our glasses of complimentary tap water. I wondered whether this meal counted as authentic Swiss cuisine.

"What's the plan tomorrow, Dad?" asked Candi.

"I'll log onto Google Maps before we leave and make notes about the route to Liechtenstein. On the way, we can visit the pretty town of Lucerne, where there are medieval bridges with beautiful paintings."

Candi scrolled on her phone and showed it to me. "Are these the bridges?"

I inspected the photo. "Those are the new ones."

"What d'you mean? I thought you said they were medieval."

I clinked my soup spoon into my empty bowl and leant forward. "Let me tell you a story."

"Oh, no," said Ellie. "One of Dad's stories. Do we have all night?"

"Where else d'you need to go? Are you sitting comfortably? Then I'll begin."

Ellie rolled her eyes.

"Back in 1993, two friends of mine travelled through Europe, girls called Kelly and Rachel. Australians. From Queensland, like the chef."

"Get on with it, Dad," said Candi. She folded her arms. "Come to the point."

"I'm a storyteller. These things take time."

"Don't interrupt him," said Fiona, "or he'll take longer."

"So, Kelly and Rachel happily toured around Europe, following a similar route to the one we're taking, but by rail. They'd been to France and Germany, and Holland and Belgium. That's something you could do when you're older, girls. You can buy these Interrail passes and travel all around Europe cheaply; people even sleep on the trains to save money. The trains run frequently, and go to every…"

Ellie glared. "Dad. You were telling us about something which happened in Switzerland. I think."

"Oh, yes. Right. Kelly and Rachel were travelling by train around Europe. They'd reached Lucerne, which has a famous bridge called the Kapellbrücke, meaning 'Chapel Bridge' in English. From memory, it's the oldest covered bridge in Europe, dating back to the 1300s."

"Wow," said Fiona. "The 1300s. So long ago. It doesn't seem real."

"The unique thing about this bridge, and one other, newer bridge, dating from the 1400s, is they have painted triangular frames in their roofs, which depict scenes from Lucerne's history."

"What happened to Kelly and Rachel?" asked Candi. "Did they fall off the bridge and drown or something?"

"Nope. They're still alive and well, I presume. I haven't seen them for years. Maybe they're on Facebook?" I picked up my phone. "I'll check."

"Dad!" Ellie smacked the table. "The story?"

I lay my phone down. "Sorry, sorry. So, Kelly and Rachel arrived in Lucerne during summer 1993. They wanted to see the old bridges; the primary tourist attraction in Lucerne, but they decided to delay that activity until the following day and, on their first afternoon, chill out in their hostel room, which had a view over the lake. Mum and I visited before you were born, didn't we, Fiona? We hired a motorboat and drove around the shores. Such a great day."

"It was lovely," said Fiona. "Um, please finish your story."

"Yes," said Candi. "Before I die."

"Right. Kelly and Rachel checked into their backpackers, relaxed, ate some dinner and excitedly discussed seeing the old bridges."

"I can't imagine anyone excitedly discussing seeing old bridges," said Candi.

Ellie thumped her sister. "For goodness' sake, let him finish."

I lowered my voice mysteriously. "What happened next?"

"Yes," said Fiona. "We're dying to find out."

"That night, as Kelly and Rachel stayed in their hostel bedroom, a carelessly discarded cigarette started a terrible fire on the Kapellbrücke. In ten minutes, the flames destroyed the roof, the supporting beams and almost all the old paintings. By the time the fire brigade extinguished the blaze, all that remained was a charred, blackened skeleton."

"So, Kelly and Rachel never saw the bridge? Never saw the old paintings?" Fiona frowned. "How disappointing for them."

"They didn't. They returned to Australia without ever seeing them. The moral of the story," I said, holding up one finger, "is: seize the day. Strike while the iron's hot. Do it now. You never know what's around the corner. Don't put things off. Don't procrastinate. Don't be like Kelly and Rachel."

"That's seven morals," said Candi. "We get the message."

"Tomorrow," I said, "we'll see the Kapellbrücke and the old paintings ourselves. We'll do what Kelly and Rachel never achieved."

"How?" asked Ellie. "You said the bridge and the paintings burnt down."

I patted her shoulder. "Remember, this was a historic bridge, the prime tourist attraction in the town, and something the local people were proud of. The town council immediately decided to restore it. Lucerne without the Kapellbrücke would've been like Sydney without the Opera House. Starting with the one-third which survived the conflagration, they rebuilt the bridge in less than a year." I paused, and sipped water. "And, of course, nowadays, smoking on the bridge is banned."

The waitress cleared our plates. "Did you enjoy your soup?"

"Yes, thanks. Could we have the bill, please?"

"Of course. I will bring it."

She returned and placed a slip of paper in front of me. I opened it slowly, raised my eyebrows and handed it to Fiona.

"Sixty francs?" she said. "Sixty francs? Ninety dollars for soup and chips."

"And chicken wings," said Candi.

"Two wings each. It's a good job we didn't order the raclette. We would've spent tomorrow's food budget too."

"You guys go ahead to the room," I said. "I'll pay the bill and meet you there."

When I opened the door to our bedroom, I discovered Fiona and the girls crowded around my bed, making the kinds of noises elderly aunts might direct towards a new baby. In the centre of the fawning group, receiving multiple ear-tickles and back scratches, sat Oliver on top of my pillow.

"Get that bloody cat off my bed." I jabbed my finger. "Take him off. He's on my pillow, for goodness' sake. I have to put my head there."

Oliver shifted onto Ellie's lap.

"He's left dirty footprints. Bloody hell. Off! Off."

"Dad, he's so cold outside," said Ellie. "Let him stay tonight. He can sleep on my bed."

"Put him on your bed, then. I don't want him on mine."

"You're mean, Dad. You'd let him on your bed if he was one of those capybara things." She stroked the cat, who boiled over with purrs. "Poor Oliver."

Despite the absence of any electronic assistance, we successfully navigated the following day via a combination of hand-drawn maps, screen shots, emergency U-turns and shouting. The snow lay thick on Lucerne's rooftops as we entered the first public car park we found, and the ticket machine whirr-whirred as it vomited a small piece of paper into my hand.

"No chance of any bridges catching fire today," said Fiona. "Too cold and wet." She pulled her woolly hat over her ears before opening the car door.

I stood and glanced between the parked cars. Through the open sides of the multi-storey, the view showed flurries settling on buildings, cars and people. I zipped my jacket up as far as it would allow. The swish-swish of cars driving on the wet streets scythed through the snow-muffled scene.

"I hope we're near the town centre," I said. "I couldn't risk driving further, in case we became lost."

"We should follow the other tourists," said Ellie, pointing to a group of people exiting the car park wearing brightly coloured anoraks and carrying backpacks.

"How d'you know they're tourists?" I asked.

"They're Australians. I heard them speak. Plus, they look like tourists."

The snow fell in earnest as we pursued our fellow countryfolk across several main roads.

"I hope they're headed for the bridge." Fiona hurried to keep them in sight. "They might be going to their hotel."

Candi turned her head. "We're walking towards a river. I can hear rushing water."

The other tourists led us to the edge of a Niagara-sized torrent pouring over a weir. Paths with railings bordered the water, and imposing, stone buildings guarded the banks, the snow on their roofs and window ledges thick, white and uniformly perfect. The snow dulled sound, and our feet made a noticeable crunching sound as we traversed the pavements.

"There," I said. "The old bridge."

We ascended several steps and entered the dark interior of the covered structure. Pedestrians hurried past, their feet clumping along the wooden boards like a regiment of soldiers. I shook the snow from my coat, tugged my hood from my head and gazed upwards.

"It's weird; normal people use this every day," said Ellie, studying the ceiling of the bridge as if she inspected the Sistine Chapel. "Most tourist attractions have a fee to enter."

"Where did those other Australians go?"

"I don't know. They're not on the bridge."

"The town did an incredible job of restoring this after the fire," said Fiona. "The whole bridge looks hundreds of years old. The paintings in the roof appear faded and aged, as if they've been there for centuries."

"They have been there for centuries," said Candi, reading a sign. "This isn't the Kapellbrücke. We're on the wrong bridge."

13. FROST FAIRS

"Oh. Whoops. The sign says 'Spreuerbrücke'." I leant around her and read the information board. "The Spreuerbrücke, or Chaff Bridge, built in 1408, has forty-five of these triangular paintings. They depict the omnipresence of death."

"Nice." Candi poked out her tongue. "I'm on holiday to look at pictures of death."

We studied the paintings, then stuck our heads out of the bridge's sides and watched the river. The snow fell hard and briefly settled on tranquil water above a weir. Fiona shivered and hugged herself as we heard the torrent surge over rapids.

"D'you think the river ever freezes?" asked Ellie.

"Probably. In Holland, the canals turn into ice each year and people skate on them. And in the olden days, people held frost fairs on the frozen Thames in London."

"Did you go to those, Dad?"

"Ellie, I was born in 1969. Not 1669."

We exited the protection of the Spreuerbrücke and faced the teeth of a blizzard.

"It's so cold," said Fiona, sheltering in the lee of a public toilet. "I'm frozen."

Snow drove horizontally at us, and we joined her, squashed behind the little building. I peeked around the edge, and my face immediately took on the appearance of one of Chris Bonington's Everest expedition portraits.

"Run for it," I said. "We'll be stuck here all day, becoming wetter and colder."

We sprinted towards the Kapellbrücke, then Ellie paused to marvel at Christmas trees. "Dad, look," she said. "These trees have actual snow on their branches. It's like the fake snow people spray on trees in Australia."

I laughed. "I think you mean the fake snow resembles the real snow. Not the other way around."

The Kapellbrücke bent like an enormous arm across the river, a wooden Meccano construction kit-like lattice in this town of proud, stone, intricately painted edifices.

Tourists thronged the bridge, and we climbed slippery steps to join them. We encountered our old friends, the Australians, who'd unknowingly provided us tourist guidance services. I nodded a greeting at them, as fellow travellers do when miles from home, then realised, despite the fact they'd played such an important role in our tour of Lucerne's sights, they'd have absolutely no idea we existed. Printed signs helpfully pointed out which paintings had been saved from the fire and which were reproductions, and the swirls of the river rushing around the bridge piers echoed below.

Halfway along the bridge, a sturdy, stout, stone tower stood in the middle of the river with water sluicing around it.

"This stone tower," Fiona read from an information board, "is older than the Kapellbrücke itself. It was built in 1360."

"They should've built the bridge out of stone as well," said Ellie. "It wouldn't have burnt down then. Silly people."

Candi leant through a slot in the side of the bridge and snapped some photos. She scrolled and uploaded them.

"Don't drop your iPhone in the river," said Fiona. "I'm not diving in to retrieve it."

I frowned. "How are you connecting to the internet, Candi?"

"This bridge has free wifi. Pretty advanced for a medieval bridge."

"Their priorities are all wrong," said Fiona. "Free wifi, but no heating. I'm heading for the supermarket to warm up." She hugged herself, and we stumped down steps at the far end of the bridge.

In countries where people speak an unfamiliar language, one of my greatest sources of schoolboy amusement is studying advertisements, grocery trademarks and road signs to find words which would seem slightly rude to an English speaker. 'Slagroom', meaning 'whipped cream' in Dutch, was a memorable menu item from Holland. 'Mini Dickmanns' were a noteworthy dessert product in Germany, and a children's colouring book with an illustration of *Bob the Builder* on the front, under the heading 'Male Bog', was my favourite from Denmark. (Subsequently, I discovered 'male bog' was Danish for 'colouring book'). I hoped Switzerland would provide additions to my collection, and chuckled to myself as I walked around the store trying to find them. My search for immature humour derailed when I became sidetracked assessing how many English phrases had become commonplace in the German language since my last visit to Europe.

'Weekend deals'.

'App downloaden'.

'Online Order'.

Surely there's a German word for 'Weekend deals'?

"Dad." Candi tugged my arm. "This Aldi has an entire shelf of Swiss chocolate. Could we buy some?"

I abandoned my linguistic studies and wandered over to my family.

Ellie scanned her eyes across the shelves. "This supermarket has a lot more choice than the ones in Australia. Look at all the different bread. You can buy produce here that isn't wrapped up in plastic. And they have hot pies and sausage rolls, and paper bags to put them in. Australia could learn a lot about recycling from the Swiss."

"Could we eat lunch now?" asked Candi, when we'd returned to the car with armfuls of bread, hot snacks, cheese with holes in it and chocolate. Tons of chocolate.

"Great," said Ellie. "Another car picnic."

I pulled my cuff back and inspected my watch. "It's 11:00 a.m. Shall we find somewhere more picturesque to eat?"

"Sounds nice," said Fiona. "But d'you know which way we drive next?"

I inspected the map we'd persuaded the receptionist at the backpackers to scribble on. "We head for Zürich. But not as far as the city. We need to turn right on this road"—I indicated a wiggly biro-mark crossing the paper—"somewhere before Zürich, and follow the shores of this lake."

The receptionist had helpfully ovalled a section of map and written 'lake' in the middle of it.

Fiona nodded. "Seems straightforward. Maybe we could eat lunch by the water?"

"Dad," said Ellie, half an hour of motorway later. "That sign said 'Willkommen in Zürich'. What does that mean?"

"Um, welcome to Zürich." I frowned.

"I thought you said we didn't drive as far as Zürich."

"We're not supposed to, no."

Warehouses and factories lined the route, and the quantity of trucks passing us increased noticeably.

"This isn't the right way, is it?" said Fiona. "You said we follow the shores of a lake. Where's the lake?"

"Maybe behind these buildings?"

Fiona shook her head at me. "I don't think so. We're lost again, aren't we? Let's find somewhere to pull over and ask directions."

"Ask directions?" said Candi. "It's amazing, the depths your generation was forced to stoop to before you had technology."

"Put a sock in it, Candi," I said. "You're not being helpful."

In the distance, I observed the knight in shining armour of every disorientated driver, the salvation of the misplaced motorist, the mediator of every arguing front seat-couple, the wonderful, relieving sight of a motorway petrol station.

"Who needs the toilet?" I asked, as the car veered into the forecourt and halted.

"Me," said Ellie. "I'm busting." She opened the car door and ran to the shop.

I held the map, and Fiona compared it to the images of Google Maps I'd screenshotted at the hostel.

"These are so tiny," she said, spreading her forefingers across the phone to enlarge the pictures. "I don't know how you thought you'd navigate from these."

"I'd memorised the route. Highway number fourteen towards Zürich, and a right turn onto highway number three."

"You obviously didn't take the right turn. Ask the petrol station staff for directions. Or buy a road map of Switzerland in the shop."

"I'm not buying a road map now. We'll leave Switzerland soon, and hopefully the SIM'll start working again and Kylie'll wake up from hibernation."

"Fill up with fuel while we're here," said Fiona. "Where's Ellie?"

"She went to the toilet."

"Yes, but she's been ages. I hope she's okay."

"When I pay for the fuel, I'll look for her."

I stepped out of the driver's door and unclipped the nozzle.

Ellie wasn't in the shop. The attendant spoke no English, which tested my language skills to the limit. For some reason, loud, German, 1980s music played from speakers in the petrol station's ceiling, making communication even more challenging. "Neunundneunzig Luftballons," sang German pop singer Nena enthusiastically, while I tried to make the attendant understand I needed directions to Liechtenstein, a location which drew a complete blank. Austria was my next option, and she entered a lengthy monologue which listed a series of complicated manoeuvres, including the execution of a U-turn somewhere in my impending future. I caught the word 'verboten' more than once, which I knew meant 'forbidden'.

A queue formed behind me. I turned around and mouthed, "Entschuldigung (Sorry)," at a truck driver attempting to buy a coffee and a pie.

The attendant obviously believed I was deaf and repeated her instruction manual loudly to counteract the crescendo of Nena's number one hit.

In the brief break while 'Neunundneunzig Luftballons' morphed into Scorpions 'Rock you Like a Hurricane', Ellie arrived at my side.

"The toilet wanted me to insert a token to enter, but I didn't have money to buy one, so I jumped through the barrier behind another lady." She panted. "I couldn't escape until someone else left. Being stuck in there was horrible. I never want to go to prison."

I threw my arm around her. "I'm sure you won't have to. Come on, let's find somewhere nice to eat lunch."

We returned to the car, and I pulled out of the forecourt onto the freeway.

"Did the attendant give you directions?" asked Fiona.

"I believe we have to do a U-turn somewhere ahead."

"Great," said Candi. "We're still lost."

Several kilometres of industrial warehouses further into Zürich, a wonderful, beautiful slip road permitted us to semicircle back on to the motorway in the opposite direction.

"Could we stop here?" asked Fiona, as a Shell petrol symbol approached. "I need the toilet."

"Seriously? You could've gone five minutes ago with Ellie." I pulled into the second petrol station of the morning.

"I didn't need to then."

"You must buy a token, Mum," said Ellie.

"I'll jump the barrier like you did." She opened the door and sprinted to the shop.

I wrinkled my nose as the smell of trucks refuelling permeated through the air, and vehicle doors slammed.

"Could we have lunch now?" asked Candi.

"What, here? In this petrol station, by the side of a motorway?"

"Yes. It's one o'clock. I'm starving."

"All right, pull it out."

Candi tugged out the snacks we'd bought in Lucerne, while I re-inspected the scanned images of Google Maps.

My mouth formed a straight line. "I see where we went wrong. We missed the turn to the three, came up the four, joined the one and ended up on the three-W."

"Why can't the roads in Europe have names, instead of numbers, like they do in Australia?" asked Ellie. "Less confusing."

I set the phone down. "This'll be easy now. We rejoin highway three in ten kilometres, which takes us all the way to Liechtenstein. No more becoming lost."

Ellie rolled her eyes. "We're always lost."

Fiona opened the passenger door and frowned at us. "I thought we were eating lunch by the side of a lake?" she said. "Not in a petrol station."

Candi spat crumbs over the back seat. "If Dad hadn't taken a wrong turn, we wouldn't need to."

Ellie thumped her. "If you waited for lunch longer, we still could have."

"Could everyone stop bickering?" I said. "We're on holiday."

"It's a direct route to Liechtenstein now," I said, as the warehouses and factories thinned out.

Fiona inspected the road signs. "Provided you don't get lost again."

"I'm not going to get lost. It's one road all the way, and only an hour's journey. Then we'll be in… oh, look. We need to pull off the motorway at this exit. Right now."

14. WONDERLAND

"Why are we diverting?" Fiona glanced back at the freeway. "Are you lost again? I thought you said it's one road to Liechtenstein."

"You're going to love this," I said. "You too, kids."

Candi leant forward. "What, Dad? Where are we going?"

"Probably another petrol station," said Ellie.

"Definitely not. We passed a sign that said, 'Lindt Factory'. I thought that deserved an urgent detour."

"Are you serious?" Fiona grinned. "I hope there's an outlet shop."

"I guarantee there is." I patted her leg. "And d'you know what?"

"What?"

"If I hadn't missed that right turn, and we hadn't accidentally driven towards Zurich, we'd never have seen it."

"You're so clever, Dad." Ellie rolled her eyes and puffed. "What would we do without your sense of direction?"

After multiple U-turns and an exciting diversion through a housing estate, we pulled into the car park of a vast, white, factory. Lights shone from a shop attached to its ground floor, and a man wearing a sheepskin coat exited, wheeling a trolley piled high with colourful wrappers.

We entered, and Candi and Ellie high-fived.

Stacks of chocolate in unfamiliar packaging reached from floor to ceiling. An entire display comprised nothing but chocolate Santas, sized from Christmas stocking-filler to small child-height. The intense, luxury, chocolaty smell reminded me of Christmas shopping in Selfridges' food court. Piles of Lindt balls in every colour wrapper filled industrial-proportion hoppers.

Dark-blue. Pale-blue.

Grass-green. Mint-green.

Rose-gold. Champagne-pink.

Purple.

Silver.

White.

Pistachio.

"I think I've died and gone to heaven," said Candi.

Fiona grinned. "Me, too."

"Hello," said a lady wearing an apron with a company logo. "Welcome to the Lindt Factory Shop."

I wanted to inquire if she was Mrs Willy Wonka.

"Would you like a free Lindt ball?" She offered us a brimming basket.

We politely selected a single ball each. Fiona desperately hoped the lady would look the other way so she could grab a handful.

I swept my gaze around the emporium. "Where do we start?"

"More to the point, how long do we have?" asked Fiona. "I'll need a week."

"Um, the shop shuts at five. Three hours."

Fiona pointed. "Grab a trolley, girls. Quick."

We meandered through the pick-and-mix section, selecting the round globules of heaven and dropping them into a dustbin liner-sized sack.

"Dad, they have fig and lime flavour." Candi held up a pale-green ball. "I haven't seen it in Australia."

"There's a lot here we don't have in Australia."

"How many of each flavour should we take?" asked Ellie. She weighed the bag up and down in her hands.

"Um, maybe one each?"

The girls plopped in four of every colour ball and measured it on a machine which calculated how much we'd spent.

"It's over one hundred euros," declared Ellie, as the sack spilt over the edge of the scales.

"One hundred euros?" I inspected the display to confirm her assessment. "How many did you put in there?"

"Four of each flavour, like you told us. There are so many types."

"Too much. Take some flavours out. Maybe aim for half."

Ellie plunged her hand in and selected balls to be sacrificed. She placed them back in the appropriate piles.

"Hey, not fair," said Candi. "She's removing all the ones I chose."

Fiona wagged her finger. "Can you two work it out between you?"

Negotiations commenced in the style of one of the more contentious discussions in the European parliament, and the eventual adjudication included someone being allowed to take a bite from one side of a pistachio-flavoured ball, then handing it to their sibling to finish.

As the cashier bagged up our purchases, she slipped four crème brûlée-flavoured Lindt balls into our bags. Fiona gave me a subtle thumbs-up.

The route became more mountainous. A winter wonderland surrounded the road: snow-covered trees, icy peaks and perfect white-linen-bedsheet fields. I almost expected Santa and his reindeer to appear from behind the pines.

We jumped, as the sound of Mariah Carey blaring 'All I want for Christmas is you' interrupted our reverie.

"Bloody hell." I thumped the dashboard. "I had hoped we'd left her in France."

"You know what this means?" said Fiona, grinning. "The SIM's working again. We've connected to a Liechtenstein telecom."

To the accompaniment of Ms Carey's delightful squawking, we crossed the border into the girls' country number twenty-one.

I leant forward in the driver's seat and glanced around. "Like you two, I haven't been here before. What d'you know about Liechtenstein?"

"SIM cards work here," said Candi. "Could you hotspot me?"

I rolled my eyes. "Any other facts?"

"It's a tax haven," said Ellie. "And its name is hard to spell." She sucked her pencil and updated her diary.

"Right."

"I've been here before," said Fiona, as I steered the car into a layby and entered the accommodation address into Google Maps.

"What d'you remember from the last time you visited?" I asked her.

"Not much. We stopped briefly for lunch on our Contiki tour."

"You can't say you've been here. The rules say you must stay a night and eat the local cuisine."

"Okay, I'm here now."

"Turn right," announced Kylie.

I shook my head slowly. "Welcome back, Kylie. I'm over the moon to hear your voice again."

We wound along the main street. Utilitarian 1960s buildings and a Shell petrol station bordered the road, punctuated by the occasional traditional Alpine chalet. I peered ahead, wrinkled my nose and wondered if the entire country resembled a post-war, British shopping centre.

"Are you excited to be in country number twenty-one?" I asked.

"It's not as nice-looking as France or Switzerland," said Ellie. "I mean, it's okay, but nothing special. The Christmas decorations are pretty."

"How long to our accommodation?" asked Candi.

"It can't be far; the entire country's a few kilometres across."

"Perform a U-turn where possible," advised Kylie.

"Have we passed it?" Fiona glanced over her shoulder.

We obeyed Kylie's instruction and parked in a small tarmac area adjoining an estate agent's shop.

"You have arrived," confirmed Kylie, optimistically.

I opened the car door and zipped up my coat. Softly floating snowflakes drifted from a rhinoceros-coloured sky, and passing cars slooshed through melted snow. I pulled up my collar and swivelled.

"Are we here?" asked Fiona, from the sanctuary of the passenger seat.

"Kylie says we are, but I can't see anything resembling an apartment. Apart from this property rental shop, there's nothing except an undercover car parking space with dustbins. Hang on, there's a door at the rear."

I ran through the snow into the shelter of the gloomy area and approached the door I'd spied. A strange design etched in its frosted glass showed a caricature of a lady in Victorian clothing, with a suggestive smile on her face. I did a double-take as I realised her top was undone and her breasts rested comfortably on the lip of her corset. Cursive writing under the etching read 'Alle Ihre Anforderungen erfullt'. I knew the first two words meant 'All your,' but the others were unknown to me. Google provided the answer.

All your requirements met? This can't be right.

A brief search of the undercover area exposed three dustbins, a container with a cartoon of a rat and a metal box enclosing an electricity meter.

I returned to the car, jumped into the driver's seat and shut the door against the weather. Settled snow obscured the view through the windscreen. "This isn't right. Kylie made a mistake."

"Are we lost again, Dad?" asked Ellie.

I ignored her.

Fiona peered through the car's side window. "Were there instructions on the booking receipt?"

I scrolled through my emails. "Yes. These are so tiny. Where are my glasses? Could you read it to me?"

Fiona held my phone. "The key is in the letterbox. Use this to open the glass door with the picture of the lady. Did you find those?"

"I didn't find a letterbox, but I found the door with the lady." I glanced over my shoulder to the back seat, bent my head towards Fiona and whispered. "Her boobs are out."

"Pardon?" said Fiona. "I didn't hear you."

I whispered louder. "The lady has her boobs out."

"What are you two talking about?" asked Candi. "Is this the right place? Can we go inside? It's cold. And I'm hungry."

I cleared my throat. "Um, yes. Sure. We need to find the key. It's in a letterbox. Could you help me?"

Candi and I ran through the snow back to the undercover area.

"There's no letterbox here, is there?" I glanced around with my hands on my hips.

"Maybe they meant this metal box?" Candi opened the electricity meter cover. "Nope. No keys here." She reached towards the rat cartoon.

"Don't touch," I said. "It's poison. I'm sure they wouldn't have put them there. Keep looking."

Candi opened each rubbish bin, but we didn't find a key. Or a letterbox.

"Are you sure this is the right place?" she asked.

"Yep. The instructions say the key opens the glass door with the picture of the lady." I pointed.

"Lady of the night, I reckon," said Candi, inspecting the glass door. "Is there a phone number?"

I dialled from my Spanish phone to a number in Liechtenstein.

"Guten Abend," said a deep, croaky voice. I had an image of a Teutonic Herman Munster.

"Guten Abend. Um, we are staying at your apartment tonight. We are outside, but we cannot find the key."

"It is in the letterbox."

"There is no letterbox."

"Where are you, exactly?"

"Outside the door with the, erm, lady on it. In the undercover area."

"Walk out to the car park."

"Okay." I poked my head into the blizzard.

"See the house agent shop?"

"Yes."

"There is a row of letterboxes."

I pulled up my hood and strode to the front of the shop, where three rows of five squares resembling safety deposit boxes stood on a metal stand.

"Find the letterbox with the same picture as the door," said Herman.

The bottom right square box displayed a similar design to the well-endowed Victorian maiden.

"Found it." Among colourful flyers displaying people of all genders wearing various black rubber and leather outfits, I discovered a fluffy keyring resembling a set of handcuffs.

"Thank you," I said, but Herman Munster had already terminated the conversation and returned to the underworld.

"Grab the bags," I shouted at Fiona and Ellie through the car door. "We're in."

"I hope it's warm." Fiona tugged our luggage from the boot. "This sleet's stinging my face." She ran into the undercover section.

"I've connected to the wifi, but I don't know the password," shouted Candi.

"I don't care about the bloody wifi." I waved my arm at Candi. "The sooner the bags are out of the car, the sooner you can find the password."

My family stood behind me, while I inserted the key into the glass door decorated with the etching of the topless Victorian lady. It swung open, and we peered into the gloom.

"This place is creepy," said Ellie. She hung back from the entrance.

I searched the hall for a light switch.

"I'm getting dungeon vibes," said Candi.

A dim, soft light illuminated the hall, and the door creaked closed behind us. Cobwebs hung from a small, golden chandelier above us, and a stale, musty smell filled our nostrils. I scraped a hand through my hair and expected *Phantom of the Opera*-type music to play in the background.

Candi stepped forward gingerly and peeked in. "There are only two bedrooms."

"Yep," I said. "A double room, a single room and a sofa bed in the lounge."

"You can have the bedroom, Candi," said Ellie. "I don't mind the sofa."

Candi stepped into the smaller bedroom and backed out quickly. "Mum, there's a stripper pole by my bed."

"Seriously?" Fiona poked her head into the room, which was painted dark red, with a black ceiling. "Perhaps it's something else."

I inspected Candi's room and noted it did indeed have a slim silver pole which ran from floor to ceiling. A wooden, velvet-lined open coffin stood against the wall.

"Why did I have to choose the bedroom?" she asked.

Ellie tapped her shoulder and pointed. "I'm not sure my room's better."

Dark-wooden furniture cluttered the windowless living room. Two-pronged gold-coloured candelabras jutted from the walls and unusual, Gothic ornaments guarded the corners. A pile of vinyl records lay scattered across the sofa.

"What is this place?" asked Candi.

"No idea," said Fiona's voice from the double bedroom, "but if you think your rooms are weird, have a look in ours."

15. FROZEN

We hesitated, then entered the main bedroom.

I stood with my mouth open. "What the hell?"

Against one wall stood a perfectly normal double bed, covered with a gold bedspread. At its foot, a wide, sliding window at chest height led to a tiny, raised, outdoor courtyard. There was no way I could find to access the external area except by climbing out of the window. Entirely filling the courtyard, a long couch allowed its occupants to relax and enjoy a ring-side view of any action taking place in the double bed.

I slid open the window to investigate further, and a blast of cold air hit me in the face.

"Shut that right now," said Fiona. "At least this place is warm."

"I am glad," said Ellie, "we're only staying in Liechtenstein one night."

The snow had already melted on the pavements as we returned to the cobbled streets of Vaduz for a pre-dinner excursion. A gigantic Christmas tree covered in twinkly yellow lights stood outside the principal municipal building, so we photographed it from different angles. We photographed the building, which was attractive in a classical European way. We photographed ourselves in front of the Christmas tree. We photographed ourselves in front of the building. Neither was going to do anything more spectacular, so we stopped photographing them.

"Is that it?" asked Candi. She pressed her lips into a straight line, as a bus paused in the road next to us, and its engine chugged while a line of traffic formed behind it.

"Is what it?" I asked.

"Liechtenstein? Have we seen it now?"

"Possibly. It's a tiny country. About forty thousand people live here. Among the smallest countries. Sixth smallest, I think."

"What's smaller than this?"

"The Vatican's the smallest. Then, Monaco. Not sure what's next."

"Does Liechtenstein have a king?"

"Nope. A prince. The country's full name is the Principality of Liechtenstein. He's one of the wealthiest monarchs in the world."

Fiona pointed directly upwards. "And there's where he lives."

We craned our necks vertically. Above the municipal building with the pretty Christmas tree, dim lights shone through the dusk and illuminated towering, white walls high on the cliff above us.

"That's his house?"

"His palace, or castle."

We stepped back to reduce pressure on our necks.

"It's like our apartment," said Ellie.

"What d'you mean?"

"The apartment contains the sofa outside the window, keeping an eye on what's happening in the bed. The Prince's palace is the sofa. The country of Liechtenstein is the double bed. The Prince can keep an eye on what's happening in his country from his vantage point."

"Right. Interesting comparison. Let's see what else we can find here."

The pedestrianised street contained shops which were about to close for the night, and a tourist information centre, which was also about to close for the night.

Fiona pushed the door, and a young, primly dressed lady behind the counter immediately stood to attention.

"Hello," said Fiona. "Are you still open?"

"Yes," said the lady, her voice strongly Germanic, "but only for another ten minutes."

As we entered her shop, I concluded we were the first tourists she'd seen today. Possibly for a month. Although the information centre contained modern shop fittings and bright lights mounted in its high ceilings, the offerings on the shelves hadn't been touched for decades. Miniature models of the Prince's castle, mugs with flags on them and postcards of views which the weather would never permit us to see gave a distinctly 1970s aura. Candi wound a musical box, which played a plinky tune that might've been the Liechtenstein national anthem for all we knew.

We wandered between the displays and picked things up politely, in the sure knowledge we weren't planning to buy anything. At the very least, we were rearranging the dust.

"How long are you in Liechtenstein?" asked the assistant.

"We're driving to Austria tomorrow."

"Ah, Austria," she said, as if this was somewhere she longed to flee to. "It is a shame you are not staying more days. There is a lot to do here."

"There is?" I said, which may have been a slightly rude reaction. I had a brief flashback to my encounter with the Franco-German Luxembourg tourist information man.

"Yes. There is a modern art gallery called the Kunstmuseum and the Liechtenstein National Museum. There is a stamp museum, a ski museum and a rural life museum. And a library."

"Can we visit the castle?" asked Fiona. "Its lights on the mountain look amazing on top of the cliff in the dark. Like a scene from *Where Eagles Dare*."

"No, sorry. The castle is not open to visitors. I am closing now, but if you come back tomorrow, I can tell you about the different museums."

I tilted my head from side to side. "Um, okay. Maybe."

"They are interesting. Please come back."

"Thank you. We might."

We left her to her dusty ornaments and stood on the pavement.

"Would you like to see the museums tomorrow, girls?"

"Museums? Boring," said Candi. "Can we buy dinner now?"

As we'd exhausted all the attractions available on a snowy winter's night in Liechtenstein, we returned to the car.

"I've never seen groceries as expensive as this," said Fiona, as she inspected the fresh produce section of Liechtenstein's supermarket. She shook her head and picked individual vegetables from the display baskets. "I fancied cooking something nice, but I can't justify spending fifteen dollars on a bit of cabbage. Swiss food is apparently a big influence here, but this place makes Switzerland seem cheap." She weighed the cabbage-quarter in her hand and replaced it.

"The frozen stuff's more reasonable." I opened a glass-fronted freezer and pulled out a family-sized tray of meatballs from a cloud of condensation.

"Looks like dinner's Swiss meatballs," said Fiona. "Traditional Liechtenstein food."

"Better than cabbage," said Candi.

We grabbed a bottle of Gewürztraminer and returned to the brothel to drink it with our meatball dinner.

After dinner, I curled up in bed with my capybara book, and cast occasional glances at the voyeuristic aperture in case anyone had arranged a booking to watch me.

"Fiona," I said quietly.

"What? I was almost in dreamland."

"This book says capybaras can be successfully house-trained, like cats and dogs."

"That doesn't mean you're getting one. Go to sleep."

"Is there anything else you'd like to see in Liechtenstein?" I asked, as we shared a box of cereal in the morning.

"Can we escape as quickly as possible?" Ellie shuddered. "I'm so creeped out by this place. I'm not sure I slept at all."

"Me neither," said Candi. "Where are we going today?"

"If you took your face out of your phone and listened to more family conversations, you'd know," said Fiona. "The next country's Austria."

I sipped my coffee. "What d'you know about Austria, girls?"

"Hitler came from there," said Candi. "He was the leader of the Nazi party and dictator of Germany from 1933 to 1945."

"Very good. I'm having Frankfurt airport déjà vu. And I'm sure that's not the number one thing Austrian citizens proudly advertise about their country. Anything else?"

"They generate sixty percent of their power from renewable energy," said Ellie. "Better than Australia."

"Do they? I guess they must have hydro facilities, because of the mountains."

"I hope we see them," said Candi. "The beautiful scenery you keep telling us about hasn't exactly been visible."

"You saw some in Interlaken."

"For a minute, through the clouds. I need a photo of me like this for my feed." She turned her phone around and showed me a picture of a tanned Kim Kardashian-like model dressed in pristine white ski gear which had clearly never been used for skiing. She posed in front of icing-sugar peaks under a Microsoft Windows-blue sky.

"Um, no. I will admit we haven't seen anything like your photo yet. Or, for that matter, anyone. Let's hope the weather's better in Austria."

Ellie nodded. "And the accommodation."

Two minutes after heaving our bags out of the brothel, Kylie steered us across the border.

"Goodbye, Liechtenstein." Fiona waved. I dismissed a thought of a more appropriate gesture.

"I'm not sure I'm bothered about visiting country number twenty-one again," said Ellie. "I think we saw it all."

"Mariah Carey's Christmas album, anyone?" Fiona winked.

"Nooo!" Ellie, Candi and I shouted simultaneously.

"Okay," said Fiona, scrolling through my phone. "Seeing as we're surrounded by snow, how about this?"

To the soundtrack of 'Let It Go' from the movie *Frozen*, we progressed through increasingly scenic Austria. The cloud lifted and revealed Alps whitened to the foothills, although the taller peaks remained shrouded. I drummed the steering wheel, peered forward and grinned.

"These mountains are amazing," said Candi. She stared with her hand flat on the window and attempted to take a photo from the car. "I hope we find free wifi soon."

"There'll be plenty of photo opportunities once we stop," said Fiona. "You won't snap a good one while we're moving."

"What if the cloud descends again? These could be the best pictures I take all holiday."

She turned to Ellie. "Can you snap me with the mountains in the background?" Candi posed, as Ellie raised the phone.

Immediately, everything turned black.

"What happened?" asked Candi, looking over her shoulder.

"We've entered a tunnel." I pushed my sunglasses onto my forehead.

"Are we inside a mountain right now?" asked Ellie. "That's so cool. And scary, to think of the weight of rock above us."

"What about my photos?" asked Candi. "How long's the tunnel?"

"A sign at the start said fifteen thousand metres," said Fiona.

"Fifteen thousand metres? Fifteen thousand? How many kilometres is that?"

"Duh," said Ellie. "It's fifteen, obviously."

The A12 motorway exited the tunnel and wound through a deep, wide valley, sandwiched between the Nordkette mountains on one side and the Tyrolean Alps on the other.

"I'm loving country number twenty-two," said Ellie. She gazed in every direction through the windows and forgot to blink. "And we haven't left the car yet."

"Me, too," said Candi, snapping enough pictures of snow-capped peaks to last Kim Kardashian the remainder of her Instagram career. "How long until we arrive at our next stop?"

"Twenty minutes maybe?" I said. "Our route'll leave the main road and climb into the mountains. We're staying in a ski resort, remember?"

"And tomorrow we're skiing?" asked Candi.

"Yep."

"I can't wait," said Fiona. She jiggled in her seat. "I'm sure skiing will be easier here than at home."

"Mum," said Ellie. "You are *not* skiing again. I won't let you."

"Aw," said Fiona. "But I've brought all my ski clothes. I'm wearing them now."

"Don't you remember last time? You fell off the end of the chairlift, couldn't control your descent, almost skied over a cliff, crashed into that poor lady, tumbled spectacularly head over heels, lost both your skis and had to be rescued by ski patrol? And that was after your one-on-one lesson with the instructor."

"Mmm, that ski instructor." Fiona closed her eyes. "He looked like Pierce Brosnan."

"Maybe you were so busy ogling him," suggested Candi, "you didn't listen to his instructions?"

"We're not going through that again," said Ellie. "It ruined the day for all of us."

Fiona pushed out her bottom lip. "You don't have to come with me. You do your own thing. I'll go by myself."

"No way." Ellie tossed her hair. "We'll lose you and never see you again. Find something else to occupy your time while we're skiing. Maybe shopping, or sightseeing?"

"We'll see," said Fiona. "I think I'll be fine."

Kylie instructed us to leave the freeway, and the road wound gently upwards. On a tight bend, we passed a public bus with the letter 'J' illuminated on its display, full of standing passengers dressed in ski gear. As we entered Igls ski village, Alpine chalets framed both sides of the route, with skis stacked outside. Their pine-wooden exterior and colourful window shutters contrasted against the white-cloud-with-light-blue-holes sky. We turned our heads left and right, drinking in a view we'd only seen before on *The Sound of Music*.

"Look at the snow piled on the house roofs," said Ellie. Her eyes gleamed, and she grinned at every fresh sight.

"Funny name, Igls," said Candi. "Sounds like a kids' rock band."

"It's pronounced 'Eagles'," I said. "Which sounds like an adults' rock band. It's a famous ski resort. It hosted the winter Olympics twice in the '60s and '70s."

"Seriously?" asked Candi. "We're skiing on an Olympic run? I need pictures of me next to the Olympic rings."

"Mum's not skiing." Ellie shook her head.

Blue sky holes in the white cloud displayed jagged lines of mountains plopped into the valley as we stepped out of the car and observed the concrete blob of Innsbruck far below us.

"I wonder where we find the key to the apartment? How do we enter?" I searched around the entrance for a key box.

"I'm getting Liechtenstein vibes," said Candi.

At that point, we made the acquaintance of Birgit.

16. GLÜHWEIN

A lady exited the doors to the apartment block. "Herr Prior? Guten Tag. My name is Birgit." She inspected her watch and frowned. "I haff been vaiting for you."

Thin and aged around fifty, with bleached-blond, short hair, small, rectangular glasses and immaculate dress sense, she stood on the front step with her arms folded.

"Hello." I held out one hand. "We weren't expecting anyone to meet us. We imagined we'd let ourselves in."

Despite the fact the clock had recently ticked past the check-in time of 2:00 p.m., we were late. With a capital 'L'.

"Nein," said Birgit. "I greet all my guests. You will not understand how things work."

"Um, okay." I glanced down. "Thank you."

She pointed accusingly at the Peugeot. "It is strictly forbidden to park here. The correct place is the next turning, up the street."

I shuffled my feet. "Er, may we unload our bags?"

"It will be okay. You must move it when you finish. Do not leave it here overnight."

"I promise I will move it." I stood with my hands clasped in front of me like a schoolboy who's been caught hiding a mouse in a girl's lunchbox, and wondered if Birgit would make me write out my statement one hundred times.

She jangled a set of keys at me, secured to a large, red, plastic disc. "I have attached this keyring, so you do not lose them, ja?"

I realised they'd be far too big to fit in my pocket and hoped I could discard the huge attachment once she'd departed.

"The big one," continued Birgit, confiscating the bunch again and holding up a metal key big enough to unlock Westminster Abbey, "is for the outside door. Here, I show you how it works."

We followed her up the steps and watched as she inserted the key, turned it anticlockwise and rotated a brass handle.

"Thanks," I said. I made to take the keys from her.

"Nein, Herr Prior." She grasped hold of them and locked the door again while we were still outside. "You must show me you can do it."

I briskly demonstrated to Birgit this wasn't the first time I'd ever opened a door with both a key and a handle, and hoped we weren't going to have to execute everything twice to prove we were suitable tenants.

At the back of the communal hall, a pair of elevator doors stood with a staircase to their right.

"It is better if I show you the lift," said Birgit. "To call it, press this button."

She pushed the one thing that resembled a button in the entire area, a circular, brass-coloured knob embossed with an up arrow. The lift opened, Birgit held the door, and we squished ourselves around our luggage.

"I'll take the stairs," said Fiona.

"Nein," said Birgit. "You must come in the lift too, so you see how it works."

Fiona obediently folded herself in, and the doors slid closed.

"Your apartment is on the second floor, Herr Prior, so which button do you think will take us there?"

"Number two?" I suggested.

"Very good," said Birgit, as if she addressed a kindergarten child who'd successfully extruded his first solo poo. "Please press number two."

With a jerk, the lift began a reluctant ascent. The doors opened at level two, and we dragged our bags into a small corridor with three identical doors.

Birgit annexed the keys again.

"You are in apartment number four. The small, silver key opens the top lock. Once you have undone that, the brass key opens the bottom lock. You must turn this handle at the same time as turning the brass key. I will show you, then you will try."

She turned the key in the top lock and glanced over her shoulder to ensure all four of us had taken sufficient note of her demonstration. I glared at Candi, who studied her phone, out of fear Birgit would enact the entire process again until we'd achieved the required mark in the exam.

"And the bottom lock and handle like this."

The door swung open, and I picked up my bag.

Birgit wagged one finger from side to side. "Nein. We do not enter yet." She closed the door. "Now, you try with the key."

I raised my eyes at Fiona, who'd looked sideways and bit her lip. My door-opening demonstration passed Birgit's approval, and we entered a large living area with high ceilings and a tiled floor, traditionally furnished in light-brown wooden furniture. Three windows faced in two different directions and flaunted a view of snow-covered neighbouring chalets against a background of distant snowy foothills.

"This is an improvement on last night," Candi whispered to Ellie. They marched to the windows, leant forward to gaze in every direction and snapped pictures with their phones.

I dangled the huge keyring at Birgit. "Thank you," I said. "This looks lovely. We'll unpack and buy groceries."

"Nein," she said. "I must show you how everything works. Let's start in the kitchen. Who will cook?"

"I do all the cooking," said Fiona.

I started to mutter I wasn't a completely incapable husband who couldn't heat a tin of baked beans, when she winked at me. My very smart wife had offered herself as a human sacrifice to receive Birgit's lengthy demonstration alone, which gave the rest of us a chance to unpack.

"I've found our bedroom," said Candi. She dumped her bag in a room which contained two single beds. Ellie followed her, and they both plugged in their phone chargers.

Fiona made suitable exclamations of comprehension in the kitchen, followed by the unmistakable beeps of a microwave oven. Clearly, my best course of action was to remain hidden until the explanation completed. I sat on the double bed and read the guest information, which Birgit had written in a similar vein to her lectures. Its eighty pages of detailed instructions would've formed holiday reading for a week, so I skipped ahead to the bus timetable.

Birgit's voice came from the kitchen, saying, 'Nein' several times to Fiona. Concluding it wasn't safe to emerge yet, I opened our suitcase and had begun to separate our clothes into a pile we hadn't worn yet and a pile requiring washing when I discovered my kindle, so I lay down to read more facts about owning capybaras.

Around the point where I realised the book was American, and my desire to own a capybara in Australia might not be legal, Fiona's period four in oven operation approached afternoon bell time, and I poked my head out of the sanctuary of the bedroom.

"Thank you for showing me everything." Fiona shook Birgit's hand. "I'm sure we'll be fine now."

"Is there a laundry here?" I asked, my arms full of dirty clothes.

"Oh," said Birgit. "I have forgotten to show you. Please, follow me."

Fiona glared in my direction as Birgit began a detailed run down of the precise operation of a washing machine.

"Before we buy groceries," said Fiona, her eyes gleaming, "let's visit the ski hire shop. If they can fit us for skis this evening, we won't waste valuable snow time tomorrow."

Ellie folded her arms. "Mum, please. No skiing. Austria's not ready for the carnage."

"Why should you have all the fun? I'll ask the ski hire staff how difficult the slopes are."

Four deep bells sounded as we crept along a slippery pavement towards a church with a blue clock on its pointy tower. The path expired and forced us into the road where we nipped single file around a restaurant displaying stags' horns mounted on the outside. We discovered the ski hire shop in an alpine-style building directly behind a bus shelter.

Fiona examined the timetable. "The J bus runs to the mountain from this stop. We can collect our skis in the morning and hop straight on." She hugged me and grinned. "I can't wait."

"Um, sure," said Ellie. "Can you carry a pair of skis without jabbing your fellow passengers' eyes out?"

Candi pushed the ski shop door, and a miniature cowbell jangled. Our cheeks defrosted in the warm air blowing from a heater above the entrance, and a faint chemical smell wafting from a back room reminded me of hairspray.

A tall man with a stubbly face nodded at us. "Guten Abend."

He wore a thick, bright-red apron and wiped grease from his hands onto a grey cloth.

"Hello," said Fiona. "Please, may we rent some skis?"

"Of course. Where are you visiting from?"

"Melbourne, Australia."

"Ah," he said, "I was there a few months ago. I work at Mount Buller when it is summer here and winter there." He held out his hand to shake. "I am Wolfgang."

"Mount Buller?" I shook my head slowly. "Our local ski resort. Three hours from our home."

"Kleine Welt," said Wolfgang. "Small world. How long are you staying?"

"Two nights. We'd like to ski Patscherkofel mountain tomorrow. We'll need skis, boots, poles and helmets."

"No problem. Will you all be skiing?"

"Yes, please," said Fiona.

"Stop, Mum," said Ellie. She turned to Wolfgang. "Is Patscherkofel easier or harder than Mount Buller?"

"It is steeper," he said. "Patscherkofel has red runs, which you do not have in Australia."

Ellie planted her hands on her hips. "Mum, you're definitely not skiing. You struggled on the greens and blues; there's no way you'd manage a red run. You'll break your leg. Or somebody else's."

"What am I going to do?" Fiona shrugged. "I'm not sitting at the bottom while you enjoy yourselves. I want to have fun in the snow too."

Wolfgang rubbed his chin. "What about cross-country skiing? There are some nice trails."

"I'm not sure. I've heard it's agony on the thighs."

"Yes," said Wolfgang, "it can be. The other option is snowshoeing." He opened a locker and produced two bright-green, plastic contraptions. "Here. Try these on."

While Wolfgang fitted Candi, Ellie and me with skis, Fiona slipped on high-tech snowshoes, the modern versions of the tennis racket-style seen in *Heath Robinson* cartoons. She clumped around the shop and poked the floor with ski sticks.

"I love these," she said. "They're so comfortable, and easy."

"Phew," said Ellie. "You shouldn't be able to do much damage with them."

"And," said Wolfgang, "when you buy your lift tickets, if you do not ski, you pay less money. Ask to buy a sightseeing ticket."

"Thank you." I said.

We stacked our chosen gear by the shop door.

"You can collect your skis in the morning," said Wolfgang. "We open at 8:30."

Fiona danced on the spot. "I won't be able to sleep."

Our trip to the small resort supermarket to buy groceries didn't result in any rude, foreign trademarks to add to my collection, but it concluded in a purchase of Austrian wine, something we'd never had.

"I wonder," said Fiona, as we lugged our shopping bags into the lift, "whether Austrian wine's anything like Gewürztraminer?"

I grinned. "I hope so, but let's save it for tomorrow night after skiing. Why don't we take the J bus into Innsbruck this evening and have a quick visit to a Christmas night market? We haven't seen one since Colmar, and that's three evenings with no glühwein."

"Great idea," said Ellie. "It's weird we didn't find a good market in Switzerland."

"Or Liechtenstein," said Candi. "We didn't see much in Liechtenstein apart from spooky brothels and frozen meatballs. I hope there's a DJ at the market here."

The Innsbruck-bound J bus hurtled down the mountain. We stood and held on, as the vehicle swerved left and right.

"I feel sick," said Fiona.

"I wonder how the ride back will feel after glühweins?" asked Ellie.

The bus dropped us outside a noisy Christmas market next to a river. We quickly purchased four emergency glühweins and leant on a railing, staring into the water. I inhaled deeply through my nose, breathed the cold Alpine air and smiled.

"It's so clear, like glass," said Fiona, gazing into the water. "You can see every pebble on the bottom."

"Look, there's a fish," said Ellie.

We followed her pointing finger. A brown-and-silver trout wafted side to side in the current, swishing its body but making no headway.

"It must mean the river's clean," said Ellie. "No pollution. The Austrians have a fantastic environmental record."

"I'll bet the fish is bloody cold." I stared across the river at the multi-coloured row of buildings on the opposite bank. "This is a pretty setting, with the mountains in the background."

"They won't be there for long," said Candi.

"What d'you mean?"

"Look." Candi pointed at the row of peaks, and, as dusk fell, cloud descended and covered them to their foothills.

I shivered. "I hope it clears for tomorrow's skiing. We haven't had much luck with Alpine views yet."

After testing plenty of glühwein to ensure the quality compared with Germany, Luxembourg and France, we bought a dessert of traditional chocolate pastry balls to satisfy our local food requirement and surfed the J bus back to the ski resort.

Light streaming through the louvre shutters woke me, and I threw them open.

"Close the things, Simon," said Fiona. "I'm still snoozing."

"Never mind that." I waved my arms, jumped up and down and pointed. "Look. Look outside."

17. SCHNEESCHUHE

"What?" Fiona squinted, rubbed her eyes and sat up.

"Look at this. No cloud. Clear day. Best we've had. Perfect for skiing." I ran into the girls' room. "Get up, quick. The sun's shining. The mountains are calling. Seize the day."

"Go away," said Candi. "Go. Away." She turned over and tugged up the covers.

"There's no cloud. You can see the mountain tops. All of them. Look." I threw open the shutters.

"Wow," said Ellie, sitting up and shading her eyes. "Time to post."

"Where's my phone?" asked Candi's duvet. Like a scene from *The Evil Dead*, a dismembered arm reached out from her covers and began groping at the floor.

"Come on." I threw clothes at her. "Hurry. Let's go skiing."

The J bus swerved violently up to Patscherkofel ski resort. This time, we carried skis and wore boots, which made bus-surfing considerably harder. I grimaced as I managed to stand on my own toe, and I grabbed hold of Fiona to balance.

"Dad, hang on to something." Ellie pulled me towards the centre of the bus.

"I can't," I said, as my ski jabbed an Austrian man. "I don't have spare arms."

"Hold both your skis in one hand. Like this." Candi demonstrated how the professionals appeared suave and composed.

"I'm glad I have snowshoes," said Fiona. She held up the green, plastic contraptions. "They're easier to handle."

The bus halted hard enough to fling every standing passenger towards the windscreen, and we staggered out to find three flights of metal stairs disrupting the route between us and the start of the ski lift.

I shouldered my skis. "Why, when ski boots feel like walking with bags of cement strapped to your ankles, and carrying skis and poles is like juggling fence posts, does every ski resort have multiple staircases to ascend before you're permitted to ski? Mount Buller's exactly the same. The staff must enjoy a good laugh watching their customers tumble and drop everything." I placed a foot on the bottom step and began my slow and comedic ascent towards the ticket windows.

The lady behind the counter spoke no English, and my schoolboy German didn't interface well with the Austrian dialect, so negotiations over lift passes took longer than I might have liked. I eventually made her understand one adult and two teenagers would be skiing, but the word 'sightseeing' stumped her.

"Zite-zeeing?" she repeated. "Was ist das? (What is that?)"

"Um, meine Frau will, um, gehen mit den Schneeshuhen (my wife wants to go with the snowshoes)." I didn't know what the German for snowshoeing was, so I hoped my cobbled-together sentence was correct, or at least comprehensible.

"Ah, Schneespeil (snow play)," said the lady with a huge grin of relief, and we arrived at a mutually acceptable agreement Fiona's pass would permit her to ascend the mountain and build a snowman.

"Remember, girls," I said, as we queued for the cable car, "this isn't like home. Here, you take your skis off and stack them in the rack on the outside of the lift."

"What?" Candi frowned. "We remove our skis every time we come down the mountain?"

"We'll spend more time with them off than on," said Ellie.

"The descent'll be far longer than the short runs we have in Australia. Don't be surprised if you're skiing for half-an-hour non-stop."

"Cool," said Candi and Ellie.

Two middle-aged Austrian couples clattered into the ski lift capsule ahead of us wearing matching, expensive-looking ski outfits. They talked amongst themselves and behaved in exactly the way I expected super-confident Austrians to act who'd been skiing this mountain since they were toddlers. The cable car creaked and swung as it rose, and I peeked through the transparent doors and grabbed Candi's arm to point out animal tracks.

As we ascended, I extracted a paper ski map and pointed at symbols. "Here's the lift we're riding now. We began at Talstation, and halfway up the mountain is Mittelstation, which is German for 'middle station'."

"I think a non-German speaker could work that one out," said Ellie.

"Yes. Mittelstation is important, as we change cable cars, and a different lift takes us up to Bergstation, at the top. Mountain station. Berg means mountain. Like iceberg; meaning ice mountain."

The cable car swung silently as the couples opposite continued to talk, nod and gesticulate at each other. I could tell they spoke German, but the Austrian dialect was incomprehensible.

Ellie leant over and tapped the map. "Look, Dad. There's a blue run down from Bergstation to Mittelstation. We could start there for practice."

"I don't need practice." I puffed. "Skiing's like riding a bike. You never unlearn it."

Ellie rolled her eyes. "Okay, Dad. Whatever you say."

The capsule slowed as it approached Mittelstation.

I stood. "Everyone ready to climb out? The cable car won't stop, it'll just slow down, so grab your skis quickly before you're carried to the bottom again."

The Austrian couples continued to enjoy their relaxed conversation. I guessed they'd had plenty of practice changing cable cars here. As the doors opened, we clambered out and grabbed our skis from the rack.

"This way says 'Ausgang'," I said, as I clumped away from the capsule. "Meaning 'exit'." I nodded expertly at the operator behind his glass screen. He ignored me.

Five seconds later, we found ourselves outside in the snow, and mountain air chilled the inside of my mouth as I breathed. Skiers swished past downhill, but nobody had exited with us.

I frowned and scanned left and right. "Where the hell's the cable car to the top station?"

"This door says 'Eingang'. Does that mean 'entrance'?" asked Ellie, pointing back to the cable car Mittelstation.

"Yes, but it goes back to where we came from."

"Um, Dad?"

"Yes, Candi?"

"There's only one cable car. It slows down here at the middle station, then continues up the mountain; we didn't have to climb out."

We trudged through the eingang, rejoined the same capsule we'd exited and again sat opposite the Austrian couples, who found our reappearance extremely amusing. The lift operator grinned and gave me a thumbs-up as the lift swung from the Mittelstation and headed upwards.

Fiona shook her head at me, and my cheeks reddened. "All right, all right. The diagram isn't clear. Look." I unscrumpled the map from my inside pocket. "See, it looks like two separate cable cars."

The Austrians nodded at us and laughed. I hoped they'd all crash into each other spectacularly, rip their expensive outfits and need to be carted away by Ski Patrol.

The views became more and more expansive as the cable car ascended further. Thomas the Tank Engine-blue sky contrasted with the all-round vista of white, jagged peaks, both in front and behind us. Wisps of low clouds formed scarves around the white-topped mountain peaks, and gullies of white snow dripped down the slopes as if a celestial cake decorator had poured cream over a trayful of craggy Christmas puddings. I grinned and pointed at the city of Innsbruck with its wonderful glühwein, chocolate pastry balls and clear, trout-filled rivers in the long, U-shaped valley below, surrounded by forests of snow-encrusted pine trees.

"We couldn't have picked a more perfect day," I repeated, as I snapped photos in every direction.

"You're right," said Fiona. "I'm going to try for the summit."

My eyes goggled, as I had a sudden flashback to a film I'd watched featuring ill-prepared climbers freezing to death in a vain attempt to reach the top of Everest.

"You're going to what?"

"Try for the summit. Look. Up there."

She pointed at a distant peak, high above the rapidly approaching Bergstation.

"Mum, you can't go by yourself," said Ellie.

"Why not? There's a trail all the way up." She pointed to the map, where a worryingly thin wiggly line snaked vertically upwards from the Bergstation towards a symbol of a mast with the words: 'Gipfelstube (nicht bewirtschaftet)' next to it.

"Hang on," I said. "Let's translate that." I opened Google Translate and waited for the screen to refresh. "'Gipfelstube' means 'summit'. I know 'nicht' means 'not'. We need to decipher 'bewirtschaftet'." I tapped on my phone. "Um, 'farmed'? The summit's not farmed?"

"It'll mean groomed, Dad," said Candi. "The summit trail isn't groomed. Like going off piste."

"Off piste?" I stared at Fiona and grabbed her arm. "You can't go off piste. People die going off piste."

She gave me a withering look, while the cable car swung into an undercover area and slowed.

"Grab your skis," I announced. "Time to exit."

The doors opened.

"Are you sure we don't stay on for another ride?" asked Candi.

I puffed. "Hilarious."

The entire population of Innsbruck had turned out for this perfect, sunny Saturday, and crowds of excited, chattering skiers jostled for space. We waddled out and claimed a square metre of slush close to an outdoor dining area. The reflection from the sun shining on the snow blinded me, and I twanged my goggles onto my eyes. A coffee smell floated from the restaurant, and a small boy walked past eating a Magnum ice cream, an impressive feat as the temperature was well below freezing.

I dropped my skis, inhaled deeply and patted Fiona on the back. "What a perfect day. Simply perfect."

"Yep." Fiona performed some brief stretches and arm exercises. "I'll meet you back here for lunch."

I stared wide-eyed at the summit mast, visible a long way above us. "Are you seriously walking all the way up there?"

"Yes. Why not?"

"Your phone has no SIM. What if you trip over and break a leg? What if you slip off the path? What if you get lost?"

"Yes, Simon, and what if I'm eaten by a yeti? See you soon."

She waved and trudged away between the trees.

"Don't worry about her, Dad," said Ellie. "Be happy she's doesn't want to try skiing again. I expect the entire mountain's breathing a sigh of relief."

I snapped on my skis and stood at the top of the run. "Shall we start with the blue trail? Then take the red to the bottom?"

"Let's see how you go on the blue run, first," said Candi. "You've never skied a red."

"I've skied loads of red runs; in Italy, France and Germany." I pushed my shoulders back. "Before you were born, I was a red run expert."

"Exactly. You're old now."

"I am not old." I glared at her. "I'm 53."

I stabbed my sticks into the snow, launched myself down the slope as if I were Roger Moore in the opening scene of *The Spy who Loved Me* and immediately regretted my words.

"Come on, Dad," said Candi, skiing beside me while simultaneously adjusting her goggles. Olympic-level Austrians whizzed past. Some of them were around three years old.

"You go in front," I said. My palms moistened inside my gloves. "Wait for me at the next suitable place." I snowploughed slowly and glanced over my shoulder as Austrians continued to dodge around me, holding effortless conversations as they sped down.

The girls whizzed away, and their jackets disappeared around a bend.

I knew I had to follow them.

I knew I could ski.

I wasn't sure if I could ski like an Austrian.

18. WINTER OLYMPICS

Left.

Dodge skiers.

Right.

Dodge skiers.

Left.

Pain in knee.

Right.

Aching foot arch.

I paused to allow every Austrian on the mountain to pass me, and wished my skis made the smooth swishing sound theirs created, instead of a crunching noise as I ploughed around corners.

The girls waited at the Mittelstation.

"Where've you been, Dad?" asked Candi. "Are you coming down the red run with us?"

"Um, wasn't that the red run?"

"No; it starts here."

"I'm not sure. The red run might be too much for me."

"But you said you were an expert at red runs," said Ellie. "You skied loads of them before we were born, remember?"

"Um, I don't recall them being *this* red. I'll ride back to the top and make sure your mother's okay. You guys go ahead; ski to the bottom and tell me how difficult it is."

"Okay, Dad. See you."

"Make sure you stay together," I shouted, but my words vanished into empty air as the girls swept away, and I resigned myself to never being as good a skier as my kids.

Fiona hadn't reappeared as I exited the cable car near the top outdoor dining area. I shaded my eyes with my hands and stared up. The perfect, uniform, white slopes above me didn't betray a single human form. I sat on a spare seat at the restaurant, admired the all-round views and inspected my watch every two minutes, as the smells of soup and coffee waltzed past me in waiters' hands.

Half an hour later, Candi and Ellie joined me and pulled off their goggles.

"How was it?" I asked. "Is the red run hard?"

"It's easy," said Candi. "I took some amazing photos."

She showed me her phone.

"I think you'd be fine," said Ellie. "There are plenty of gentle parts where we whizzed along little tracks between pine trees. We even skied through a tunnel."

Candi slid her phone into her pocket. "We're going again. Are you coming?"

I gazed up at the summit, still devoid of Fionas. "I'll stay here, wait for Mum, and reserve a table for lunch. We'll have a meal surrounded by this immaculate view,"—I swept my arm in a dramatic semicircle encompassing more stunning mountains than on a Winter Olympics calendar—"then I'll ski all the way down with you. Promise."

They zipped away again.

I stared and hoped Fiona hadn't fallen over and broken her leg. Or got lost. Or been eaten by a yeti.

11:45 a.m.

Groups of chattering skiers occupied neighbouring tables, presumably complaining about how easy these slopes were for such skillful, experienced Austrians as themselves.

Where's Fiona? She's been almost two hours.

A waiter hovered at the end of my table and poised his forefinger over an iPad.

"Guten Morgen, sir. Would you like to order lunch?"

"Could I wait for my family? They're still skiing."

"You cannot reserve this table." He indicated the throngs of bright jackets swarming into the outdoor dining area. "There will be no spaces left by twelve noon. People will be waiting. Ten minutes, no more."

I stood to search for the girls and Fiona and, immediately, ski jacket-clad vultures circled. I couldn't leave the table; I'd never win the *Hunger Games* competition for another one.

11:55 a.m.

Ellie and Candi stumped up to me and banged snow off their boots.

"Hi, Dad," said Candi. "I'm starving. Can we eat?"

"We should wait for Mum."

"What? She's not back yet?" said Ellie. She gazed up towards the summit. "Where is she?"

"May I take your order now, sir?" The iPad-equipped waiter hovered again.

"Yep." Candi opened the menu. "I'll have the…"

"Wait." I stood and shaded my eyes to gaze up at the mountain. "We have to wait for Mum."

"Mama is up the mountain?" asked the waiter. His gaze wavered between us and the white slopes.

"She departed for the summit two hours ago," said Ellie.

"She is on skis?" The waiter enacted the motion of cross-country skiing with both arms.

"No. Snowshoes."

"Has she used them before?"

"First time. She rented them from the shop in Igls."

"She has gone by herself up the mountain on snowshoes, and she has never used them?" His neck muscles tensed as he pulled a face.

"Erm, yes."

The waiter leant over the railing next to our table and gazed up the mountain with us.

"What are you looking at?" asked a lady at the next table dressed in a bright-pink ski jacket. She swung her eyes in the direction of our gaze as if we'd observed the abominable snowman pop his head out from behind a rock.

"We're searching for my wife," I said. "She departed for the summit two hours ago, but she hasn't returned."

"Oh. She is lost," said the lady, unhelpfully.

"Or fallen down and broken her leg," said a fat man in a blue ski jacket opposite her, offering a similar level of Germanic reassurance. He addressed the waiter. "Könnten wir Essen bestellen? (Could we order food?)"

"This is terrible," said the waiter, scanning the slopes. "We cannot start without Mama." He gave one final glance to the summit and attended to the disobliging people on the adjacent table.

Ellie pointed into the distance. "Is that her?"

"Maybe." Candi glanced up from her phone. "It's the colour of her jacket. But that's not the way she walks."

"I wish I had binoculars," I said, as I shoved my goggles on my forehead and blinked.

"It's her, Dad," said Ellie. "She's waving."

The waiter overheard us and swivelled. "Mama is coming?"

"Yes," I sagged against the railing, "Mama is coming."

"Do you hear?" he announced to his disinterested customers. "We have found Mama."

"Wait here," I said to the girls. "Don't lose the table." I clumped off as fast as my ski boots would allow and lolloped to meet Fiona halfway.

She raised both ski poles above her head in an Olympic victory salute.

"Where've you been?" I threw up both arms as soon as she came within shouting distance. "I've been worried about you. The girls are worried about you. Even the waiter's worried about you."

"I did it, Simon. I did it."

"What did you do?"

She grinned as wide as a model in a denture advertisement.

"I reached the summit on snowshoes. By myself. Alone." She removed her gloves. "It was magical; like I stood on top of the world. Now I know what Edmund Hillary and those other mountaineers feel like. I love snow-shoeing."

"I'm so pleased you've returned safely." I escorted her back to the restaurant, where we plopped next to the girls.

The waiter rubbed Fiona's shoulder. "Mama has come," he said.

"Yes." I flopped back in my chair. "Mama has come."

"You must snow-shoe with me," said Fiona. She waved her arms like a Frenchman describing a car accident. "It's like floating on top of the snow. And it's a great workout. Feel me. I'm all hot and sweaty."

I touched her face and verified she indeed felt hot and sweaty.

"And the peace along the path; it's the best meditation." She tipped her head back and grinned. "I didn't see another person the whole time. One of the most amazing experiences of my life."

"Um, wow. We were so worried about you. All by yourself, with no means of calling for help."

"I'm walking down the entire mountain after lunch." She turned around and glanced over her shoulder. "I've checked the map, and walking trails run to the bottom."

"Gosh. You are keen."

The waiter deposited three glühweins in front of Fiona and the girls in small, transparent mugs, then he handed me a glass resembling a stately home's floor-standing vase. I removed one glove, and my hand chilled as I grasped the drink.

"That's a big beer, Dad," said Candi. "Could I have a sip?"

"Should you drink all that before skiing?" asked Ellie. "You weren't exactly steady on the blue run this morning."

"Ellie," I said, "this is the European skiing experience." I leant forward and clasped my glass in both hands. "Sitting in the sun on a clear day, the temperature hovering around freezing, drinking a beer and enjoying the Alpine scenery. Can't beat it." I gulped beer, licked froth off my lips and nodded. "And it's a nice drop. The Germans make the best beer in the world."

"We're in Austria," said Candi.

"The Germans and the Austrians make the best beer in the world." I slurped some more.

"Slow down," said Fiona. "Save some for your meal."

The waiter plopped oval bowls of soup in front of us, accompanied by a plate of thick, dark-brown bread. Steam fogged up my goggles, so I abandoned them to the glare reflected from the snow.

Candi spluttered. "Ow. This is hot." She tore off a hunk of bread and stuffed it in her mouth.

Ellie sipped tentatively. "This counts as a local meal, right?"

"Definitely." I blew on the bowl. "Excuse me,"—I flagged down the waiter—"could I order another beer?"

"Dad," said Ellie. "No."

"I'll be fine. I need something to cool the soup."

"You could've ordered water."

"Yes, Ellie. You're right. I could've done. But I didn't." I tipped my head back and finished my first beer, then persisted with the soup.

"Right," I announced, clinking my spoon into my empty bowl. "Let's do the red run." I stomped to the till and tapped my credit card, then staggered down the two steps from the restaurant into the snow.

"Are you sure about this, Dad?" asked Candi. She grinned as I wobbled. "You didn't seem confident on the blue run."

"I've never been confident… confident… confidenterer." I clipped on my skis and slid them back and forward like Eddie the Eagle at the top of the Calgary Olympic ski jump.

"Oh, no," said Ellie. "Dad's downed a couple of beers and now he thinks he's indestructible."

"It's lucky he has you two with him," said Fiona. "I'll see you at the bottom." She strapped on her snowshoes and began her swinging gait away from the restaurant.

"You two ski as fast as you like," I said. "I'll follow, and we'll meet at Mittelstation again. We'll polish off the red run."

I skied away and effortlessly performed a series of parallel turns. The girls overtook me. "Wow," yelled Candi as she passed. "You ski better when you're drunk."

"I'm not drunk," I shouted after her. Their jackets whizzed down the slope away from me.

Candi videoed as I caught up with them.

"Easy," I said. "Ready to do the red?"

"The first bit's the steepest," said Candi, slipping her phone into her pocket.

"What are we waiting for?" I skied to the top of the red run, peered over the edge, and suddenly wished I'd consumed less beer.

Or maybe more beer.

"What's wrong, Dad?" asked Ellie.

"Um, is this the only way down?" I swallowed hard and glanced to my right.

"Yep. Unless you want to ski the black run." She pointed at a slope on the opposite side of the cable car where slim, fit-looking people in figure-hugging outfits zoomed down the slopes like a clip from *Ski Sunday*.

I stared at the near-vertical drop in front of me and clenched my teeth. A row of schoolchildren aged about four skied over the crest without the assistance of poles and vanished into the distance. I wondered how they gabbled in fluent German while not crashing.

"This is the hardest bit, Dad. I promise," said Candi. "Come on, Ellie. We'll be here all day if we wait for him."

They zigzagged away while I slipped sideways down the slope. This wasn't the way the experienced skiers descended, but at least I remained upright. I wondered how I'd ever enact a turn on this near-vertical incline without hurtling uncontrollably towards the bottom.

I jumped, swivelled, and prayed simultaneously. At least one of those actions worked, and I began a barely controlled slide diagonally in the opposite direction.

"Please," I panted, as I caught up with the girls, "could we rest? My heart's in my mouth and I need new foot arches."

"Good job, Dad," said Ellie. "The beer worked."

Candi took my picture and grinned. "That's the hardest part over. The rest's easy." She skied away, and Ellie followed. I sucked in a deep breath and hoped she was right.

Snow-laden pine trees bordered both sides of this narrow, gentle section. Four snowshoers passed, the drifts crunching underfoot as they trudged uphill. I thought of Fiona, glanced through the trees and wondered whether our paths would cross. The slope became steeper, and ahead, Candi and Ellie's jackets disappeared into a tunnel. I sped up, dug my sticks into the snow several times and stuck them under my arms like I'd seen on the Winter Olympics. I tipped my head back, closed my eyes briefly and laughed.

The tunnel caused me to duck involuntarily, then I shot out of the other end and achieved the greatest dream of humankind.

The dream Leonardo da Vinci spent decades poring over.

The dream of Icarus, the Montgolfiers, the Wright brothers.

The dream of human flight.

19. HOT TUB

The flying part, for a brief second, felt marginally enjoyable.

The landing part could've been more pleasant.

One ski unclipped, and my body tobogganed headfirst down the slope on my back. Cold snow froze the nape of my neck as friction arrested my descent, and I panted, motionless like a stunned mullet. The swish, swish of other less accident-prone skiers passed on both sides.

None of them cared.

None of them stopped.

None of them checked to see if I was dead, so I presumed I wasn't.

Damage assessment required.

I pushed my goggles onto my forehead and blinked at the solid blue sky, then propped myself up on my elbows.

No blood.

No limbs at unusual angles.

A dull ache in my back, a sharp pain in my knee, and one ski.

One.

Here's another fine mess you've got yourself into.

I swivelled my head to the left, gazed up the hill and identified my lost ski a long way above me.

"Where were you, Dad?" asked Ellie, as I snowploughed towards the girls. "We've been waiting for ages. Are you okay?"

"No, I'm bloody not okay." I pointed a stick up the hill. "Why didn't you tell me the tunnel ended with a cliff? I crashed and lost a ski. My leg'll have a massive bruise now."

"Oh, yes," said Candi. "I forgot about that bit. Ready to go again?"

"Erm, are there any other ski jumps which should only be attempted by Olympic-level twenty-year-olds?"

"No, the rest of it's easy," she called over her shoulder as they skied away.

"That's what you said last time."

I rubbed my leg and took off slowly. The pine trees, thick snow and blue sky reminded me of a scene in a David Niven movie, but I paid a high price for the views.

The girls waited for me at the bottom cable car terminus.

"Is Mum here?" I asked.

"We haven't seen her," said Candi. She lifted her head from her phone and glanced around briefly. "Ready for another go?"

"Seriously? You're going again?"

"Of course. Who knows when we'll ski next?"

My leg ached, and the arches of my feet throbbed. Dancing dots of multi-coloured jackets skied expertly down the final slope, stopped exactly where they intended to and unclipped their skis effortlessly.

"I'll wait here for your mother," I said. "I hope she's okay."

A wooden bench constituted a field hospital bed, and I removed my skis and lay down. The timber dug into my back and gave me an odd combination of ache and ache relief.

I had pain in places I didn't realise I had places.

My eyes closed, and I hoped a nurse would appear on her rounds soon.

Some time later, the smell of cigarette smoke woke me. Three unshaven, scruffy men stood nearby, talking rapidly. Their dialect prohibited me from understanding every word, but I gathered they'd completed scraping snow from paths and distributing salt.

I sat up and glanced around. My phone told me it was 5:00 p.m.

Where is everyone?

A gate barred the doors to the cable car, preventing anyone else from ascending the mountain, although empty capsules continued to swing past.

Skiers chattered as they stomped down the steps to board the J bus. Back pain reminded me of my *Birdman of Alcatraz* impression. Everything hurt, and I pushed myself to my feet like a one-hundred-year-old pensioner.

I removed my goggles and gazed at the mountain slopes, as the girls swooshed to a stop in front of me.

"Hi, Dad," said Candi. "Where's Mum?"

"You haven't seen her?"

"No," said Ellie, "but guess what? You know the spot coming out of the tunnel where you fell over?"

"Yes. How could I forget? They should have a warning sign telling people about it."

"We saw someone who crashed like you did. Ski patrol stretchered them away in a helicopter. We watched it take off. It was so cool."

"Cool? Poor person. They may have broken something." I rubbed my knee and suddenly froze as I realised it could've been Fiona. "What colour jacket did they have?"

"I'm not sure," said Candi. "They were under a blanket."

"D'you think it was Mum?"

Ellie laughed. "Dad, stop worrying. People don't crash and need helicopters walking on snowshoes."

Long shadows formed as the sun disappeared behind the peaks. Staff pulled advertising boards and postcard displays into shops.

We scanned our gaze across the mountain. The dots of approaching skiers thinned. None of the dots wore snowshoes.

"Why did your mother choose a grey ski jacket?" I asked, narrowing my eyes. "I'm going to buy her a luminous orange one. With flashing lights."

"What are you staring at?" asked a voice behind us.

Fiona exited the cable car, carrying her snowshoes and grinning.

"Why did you descend in the lift?" I threw both arms in the air. "I thought you were walking down the entire mountain. We've been worried sick. Again."

She dropped her snowshoes and flipped her goggles up. "You don't have to worry about me. I'm fine."

"How were we to know? Someone had to be airlifted off the mountain in a helicopter. It could've been you. What are you laughing about?"

"Something funny happened to me," she said. "I'll tell you on the bus."

The J bus waited at the stop as we clattered down the three flights of metal steps.

"Come on," I shouted, as I tried to hold the handrail and clasp my skis and poles simultaneously. "The bus is here. Quick."

As the final queuing Austrians boarded, I arrived behind them and held the doors for my family. The bus pulled away, and we gripped the green handholds.

"Why did you ride down in the cable car?" I asked Fiona, as we lurched around the first bend. "Was it too far to walk?"

Fiona laughed again. "I followed a long, narrow track away from the restaurant through a beautiful pine forest. Because the trees surrounded me, I'd no idea where I was, or if I was aiming the correct way."

The bus paused to allow passengers to alight at a large ski lodge.

Fiona continued. "I arrived at a crossroads where three different routes headed down, and I met four people snowshoeing up the mountain. They didn't speak English, and couldn't tell me the way, so I proceeded along the most likely looking course. The path narrowed, and I'd seen no-one else for a while. I wasn't sure if I followed a proper track."

"Wow," I said. "Were you scared?"

"I knew if I kept heading downhill, I'd find my way. People's voices shouted through the trees as they skied, but I wasn't sure which direction the noise came from."

"Poor Mum," said Ellie. "There might've been wild animals in those woods. Wolves or something. Although loss of habitat probably means they're extinct here."

"Then what happened?" asked Candi. "You're here telling the story, so it's not like you died."

"I didn't see any wolves. But rounding the next corner, I did see something unexpected."

The bus stopped again, and we shuffled sideways to allow fellow skiers off.

"Don't leave us in suspense," I said. "What was around the next corner?"

"Through the trees, I saw the outline of a ski lodge, and, as I approached, I found a plump, middle-aged couple sitting in a hot tub beside it. They obviously didn't expect to see me appear, and they called out, and offered me a glühwein."

I threw one arm in the air. "Jeez, here we are, worried sick we'd have to send out search parties, and you're halfway up the mountain, getting pissed with your new mates."

Fiona ignored me. "I waved and walked over to them, and at that point I realised they didn't have any clothes on."

"What, not even swimmers?" asked Candi. "Is that legal?"

"It is in Austria," I said. "Europeans are less prudish than Australians about nudity."

Fiona nodded. "Standing fully clothed in head-to-toe ski gear, wearing snowshoes, while talking to two stark-naked Austrians is an experience I'll never forget. I gulped a glass of their wine, while politely trying to look in their direction and simultaneously not see anything I didn't want to see."

"Um, yes. That would've been difficult."

"Then," said Fiona, giggling, "the man stepped out of the tub and indicated the way to the Middle Station."

My mouth opened. "He stepped out of the tub naked? What did he point with?"

Fiona gave me a withering look. "His arm, Simon. He pointed with his arm. He'd thrown a towel around his waist. I thanked them, walked for another twenty minutes to the cable car and rode it back down the mountain." She glanced up, as the bus slowed. "Oh. This is our stop."

We halted outside Wolfgang's ski shop and clambered out.

"Anyway," said Fiona. "How was your afternoon?"

"Um, not as exciting as your nudist booze session." I rubbed my back. "I'll tell you over dinner."

Kylie guided us towards Munich the next morning.

"This is an autobahn," I said. "We can drive at any speed we like. Shall we see how fast this Peugeot goes?"

I pushed the accelerator to the floor. Expensive Mercedes and BMWs overtook us on both sides.

"One hundred and sixty so far." I grinned as I gripped the steering wheel. "How fast d'you reckon that Audi flew past? Well over two hundred?"

"Stop it." Fiona bared her teeth. "You'll kill us all. Or go to prison if they catch you."

"How? We're the slowest car on the road."

"And speeding's a strict liability summary offence," said Candi. "It doesn't attract a prison sentence. We learnt that in legal studies."

I leant forward and darted glances between the road and the speedometer. "One hundred and seventy, one hundred and eighty."

"This speed burns so much fuel," said Ellie. "Think of the environment."

"D'you reckon you'll reach two hundred, Dad?" asked Candi.

"One hundred and ninety-five, one hundred and ninety-six…"

"Dad!" shouted Ellie, glancing over her shoulder. "Police car. Behind us."

20. FESTIVAL

I glanced in my rear-view mirror and read the word 'Polizei' emblazoned on the car.

"Who cares? I'm not breaking any rules. One hundred and ninety-seven…"

"If you're not breaking the law," said Fiona, turning around, "why have they switched on their blue lights?"

"Oh, shit." I pushed the brake pedal, and the Peugeot's speed dial anticlockwised rapidly. "One hundred and thirty, one hundred and twenty…"

"They're passing us, Dad."

The police car overtook and disappeared into the distance.

"Slow down," said Fiona, as a circular road sign displaying an '80' symbol flashed by, and we entered Munich's city limits.

"Bloody hell." I sagged back in the seat. "I would've reached two hundred. I might never have the chance to speed legally again in my life."

"Yeah, well, don't get pinged for speeding now. We're in an eighty, and you're still driving at one hundred."

Ellie stared around the sparse check-in area of our central Munich backpackers' hostel. "I miss the Austrian apartment already. Even with Birgit's instructions."

Two young people barged in and dumped backpacks on the ground behind us. They chattered loudly in Spanish and scrolled through phones as they waited for us to finish. The fragrance of German pub emerged from open doors behind us, where patrons leant across a high, wooden counter topped with a single, ornate beer pump.

"Aha!" I said to my family, as I concluded negotiations with a staff member and handed out vouchers. "Here, we each receive one free drink per night at the bar, and free parking in the public garage next door."

"Are they alcoholic drinks?" asked Candi.

I read the text on the paper slip. "Yes, it includes alcohol."

"Can we drink them now?"

"Candi, it's 4:00 p.m. Let's settle into our room before we go drinking. Jeez, you're seventeen years old. Just because the legal drinking age in Europe's sixteen when you're with us doesn't mean it's compulsory to drink continually."

"But I thought you said Munich's the centre of the beer world?"

"It is. Just not at 4:00 p.m."

We stepped out of the lift and entered a starkly lit, concrete corridor with regimented rows of closed doors bordering both sides. Music from portable speakers played from a room to our left, blending with the rush of shower water and the sound of someone singing in an unfamiliar language. In the background, I heard the erratic rotating of a tumble drier.

"Here we are." I dropped a bag at my feet. "Room 101."

Fiona grimaced. "Room 101? Wasn't that the torture chamber in *1984*?"

"George Orwell's book wasn't set in Munich." I inserted the key in the lock and heaved the door open.

"Woah." Candi stepped sideways. "Will we all fit in here?"

Along the left-hand side of two-metre-wide room 101, twin sets of bunk beds were pushed against the wall. A small, square table and one chair squashed under a condensation-covered window at the far end, and the smell of pine disinfectant accompanied our entrance.

"This'll be a great life lesson for you girls," I said, as I shuffled in with my bag. "This is what prison's like. You won't break any laws after experiencing this."

"How d'you know, Dad?" asked Ellie. "Have you been in prison?"

"Um, no, but I've seen TV programs. *Porridge, Bad Girls, Prisoner Cell Block H.* The accommodation resembles this."

"It's an adventure," said Fiona. "If you girls travel after school, these are the kinds of places you'll lodge in. Dad and I stayed in loads of backpackers' hostels before you were born."

"And it's twenty-five euros each per night," I said. "Including an alcoholic drink. Stop complaining."

"I'm not complaining," said Ellie. "This'll be fun." She flung her bag onto a top bunk.

"But where's the bathroom?" asked Candi.

"Across the corridor."

"We share the bathroom?" She made mock vomiting noises.

"Yes."

"With strangers?"

"Yes. With strangers. Like our camping holidays."

"Those are different. We're not in cells." She sat on her bunk and tapped her phone. "Although the wifi works well."

"How long are you guys staying?" asked the hostel barman. He wore a flat cap, and his hipster beard brushed against his chest as he set four beers in front of us. 'Last Christmas' by Wham! played from ceiling speakers, and coloured balls clicked as customers played pool.

"Two nights."

"Are you here for the Weihnachtsmarkts?"

"Yep. We've seen amazing Christmas markets in Mainz, Colmar and Innsbruck, and we've heard Munich ones are the best."

"Tonight, you should visit Tollwood."

"Tollwood?"

"Tollwood Winter Festival."

"Sounds good. How do we find it?"

"D'you have Google Maps?"

"Yep." I showed him my phone.

"Type in Tollwood. T-O-L-L-W-O-O-D." He pointed. "It's around twenty minutes' walk. Turn right out of the hostel."

Google helpfully provided me with a sidebar of information, which I read to my family.

"A cultural festival which takes place twice a year in the summer and winter months, with each event lasting for several weeks, Tollwood aims to promote cultural diversity, environmental awareness, and social justice through artistic performances, workshops, and exhibitions. The festival's food vendors focus on organic and locally sourced ingredients, and many of them use sustainable practices."

"My kind of place," said Ellie. "An environmentally friendly festival."

"Are we having dinner there?" asked Candi. "I'm hungry."

"We could," I said. "It might be for vegetarians and vegans."

"Oh," said Candi. "Can we stop for burgers on the way?"

"No."

Along each pavement in Munich's night-time streets, a narrow path had been cleared in the snow. We walked in single file to allow space for pedestrians headed in the opposite direction. After twenty minutes following Kylie's instructions, a huge conflagration of lights, noise and people appeared. Massive Christmas lanterns hung suspended above the festivities, and crowds thronged, wrapped against the several-degrees-below-zero temperature. Queues waited at food trucks, which sold assorted Germanic hot stodge: pretzels, schnitzels, sausages, bread. I inhaled deeply through my nose and breathed in the wonderful smell of carnivorousness.

"No vegans here," said Candi. "Fancy one of those hot dogs?"

Fiona tugged my arm. "Could we watch this? I've never seen these instruments played."

Three musicians wore traditional Alpine dress, comprising black jackets fastened with a vertical row of silver buttons, black trousers and Fedora-type hats featuring a single feather stuck in one side of the band. They poised their lips over the ends of long Alpine horns, or Flugelhorns, which stretched from their mouths down to a floor stand two metres in front of them. I expected to be blasted by a noise like the Queen Mary's siren, but the gentle, melodious tunes surprised me.

"These were used to call in the cows for milking in the old days," explained Fiona to the girls.

"Nicer than roaring around the fields on motorbikes," said Ellie. "Wasn't that how you fetched the cattle on Grandad's farm in New Zealand, Dad?"

"I'm sure if Grandad had a spare Alpine horn lying around, we could've given it a couple of hoots."

"I'm starving," said Candi, part-way through the third bar of the fourth tootle.

"Me, too," I said. "What d'you feel like?"

"I feel like fruit. Or vegetables," said Fiona.

"No chance," said Ellie. "Everything here's cooked meat with bread in various forms."

"I know," said Fiona. "My stomach's crying out for fresh food. I wondered if there might've been some greens at a sustainable produce event."

"Pizza?" suggested Candi, pointing at a stall a short distance away. "It might have vegetables on it."

I nodded. "It's the most vegetable-y thing here."

We ordered from a stall where a man slid dough into the semicircular entrance of a wood-fired pizza oven, and I slurped a Löwenbräu beer which had found its way into my hand. Sparks rose from a crackling fire where people sat covered with thick rugs and swigged from large, handled glasses.

I gazed around me, smiled and lay my hand on Fiona's. "D'you realise, we're on the exact spot where we first met?"

"We are?" Fiona set down her glühwein and glanced over her shoulder.

"You met at a pizza stall?" asked Candi.

"That's not what I meant. Fiona, take a look around. D'you recognise anything?" I beamed at my wife and waited for her to react.

"Not really. It's dark."

"How about the massive tent over there? Now do you see where we are?"

"Um, no."

"This winter festival's on the same site as the Munich Oktoberfest."

Fiona frowned. "Is it? But we didn't meet at the Oktoberfest."

"Touch of dementia, Dad?" asked Ellie. "You forgot where you met Mum?"

"We travelled on the same tour to the Oktoberfest at the same time. Although we weren't officially a couple until after we returned to London. So, if it wasn't for this spot, right here, we'd never have met and you two wouldn't exist."

"Sometimes I wish Candi didn't exist," said Ellie. "OW, get off."

Fiona hugged me. "Sliding doors."

"This calls for a celebration." I tipped my glass back and headed to the bar for another round.

Fiona elbowed me in the face the following morning as she tugged clothes from our suitcase. "Sorry," she said. "There's no room to turn around. I'm headed for the showers."

"I'll take a shower too," said Ellie. "I'll hop down once you're out of the way."

Once Fiona and Ellie had departed, I sat on the edge of my bed and considered today's plans.

Today, we'd visit a memorial which profoundly affected me when I'd last seen it.

A memorial where thousands of innocent souls had lived through hell.

A memorial where thousands of innocent lives had been curtailed.

A memorial called Dachau.

In 1995, I'd travelled around Europe with busloads of other backpackers, one of whom was Fiona.

My fellow travellers' primary focus seemed to comprise tipping back alcohol, falling over and consuming more alcohol. To them, an excursion to a death camp constituted an unnecessary interruption to their drinking careers.

I couldn't subscribe to their callous attitude, their lack of appreciation of the hell millions had suffered.

At the time, I'd wanted to address the bus and shout, "Don't you give a shit? Does it mean nothing to you people died here? Don't you bloody well care?"

Fiona had attracted me partly because she shared the same sentiments.

I sat with my head in my hands and wondered how the experience would affect our teenage daughters.

The door crashed open.

"Jeez," said Ellie. "Those'd have to be the worst showers ever. The cubicle's the size of a broom cupboard. There's nowhere to hang your towel or stand your shampoo, and the shower head's out of control. Water sprayed everywhere except on me." She held up a pair of soaked track-pants.

I frowned. "Where's Mum?"

"Trying to mop up. We flooded the place." Ellie climbed into her bunk and rubbed her hair dry. "I'm not sure I'll take another shower here."

I recalled what the word 'shower' would've implied for the Nazi's captives, and squeezed my eyes closed.

A plump, blonde, rosy-cheeked server greeted us in the hostel basement dining area. She held out her arms. "Guten Morgen, meine Lieben (Good morning, my loves)," she expounded, as we arrived. I thought she might crush us in an enthusiastic embrace.

"We have for you today bread, fruit, cereals, yoghurts, meats, eggs, cheese, coffee, tea, juice. Please help yourselves." She topped up a basket full of pastries as she spoke.

I walked along the metal counter, inspecting the offerings she'd described. At seven o'clock in the morning, none of the young backpackers had risen, and we had a full choice of every food item. The wonderful, sensual smell of freshly ground coffee percolated from an expensive-looking machine on a side table.

"Wow," I said to Fiona, as I picked up a plate and wondered where to start, "all of this for six euros. Such good value."

I turned to the lady. "Vielen Dank. (Thank you). Um, is there any chance breakfast will be open before seven a.m. tomorrow? We have a plane to catch and need to be at the airport by eight."

She smiled and touched my shoulder. "Ah, Mein Lieb (my darling), no problem. I will come in early tomorrow, especially for you and your three beautiful girls." She beamed and returned to the kitchen.

"Can we help ourselves as many times as we like?" Candi asked me.

"Um, yes, in theory. We don't want to seem greedy. This isn't the Mainz Hilton."

"What's the plan for today?" asked Candi, as we sat with our plates of assorted goodies and hot drinks.

Fiona sipped a coffee. "We're visiting somewhere else which Dad and I toured at the same time without knowing it, all those years ago."

"Another pizza shop?" asked Candi.

"Far from it," I said. "Today, we're visiting hell on earth."

"We can't be." Candi grinned. "School's closed for the holidays."

I frowned at her. "It's not a joke; I need you to be serious for the next part of this trip. We're going to Dachau."

"Dachau?" said Ellie. "The concentration camp where the Nazis gassed Jews?"

"They didn't use gas at Dachau, apparently," said Fiona. "They had the facilities, but they weren't utilised."

Candi puffed out her cheeks. "Can we not talk about this while we're eating?"

"You're lucky you're able to sit here eating breakfast," said Ellie. "Those poor people at Dachau never had breakfast. One meal per day of watery soup, or boiled weeds."

"All right," said Candi. "I feel guilty now, and I'm not having seconds. Happy?"

"Yes," said Ellie. "I'm going back for seconds. You don't have to."

Snow covered the ground as we bumped into Dachau's car park, and my mouth formed a straight line as I opened the driver's door. Barely any cars joined us on this freezing midwinter's day. Duvets of white cloud hung suspended above the scene and merged with the thick, white drifts to form a monochrome scene. A plastic bag rustled as it vortexed around the gravel and spun away over the bare trees.

Bleak.
Desolate.
Godforsaken.

21. DACHAU

"These are appropriate conditions to witness Dachau." Fiona paused and hugged herself. "When we visited in the nineties, the sun shone, which didn't seem right. I still recall the silence."

"It's the same today." I glanced at the trees, stark and winter-bare. "No birds singing. Nothing. Snow always muffles sound, doesn't it? But this is eerie."

Ellie picked up a discarded Coca-Cola can and carried it to a bin. "There shouldn't be any colour here," she said. "No joy. This is a place of sadness. You feel it."

We trudged towards the iron gates separating the free world with its singing birds and colourful packaging from the world of the damned, the wretched masses, captured and condemned to the existence of the concentration camp.

The death camp.

The death camp where the greatest dream, the greatest ambition, the greatest desire was an early, pain-free grave. 'Arbeit Macht Frei' shouted the design on the gates, in the same fashion you would expect the word 'welcome' to appear at an entrance.

Work will make you free.

The biggest untruth, designed to plant a seed of hope in minds where there justifiably was none, and never could be.

Acres of parade ground, surrounded by tall, watchtowered, barbed-wire fences lay under swathes of thick, perfect, snow, unspoiled by human footsteps, animal prints or bird tracks.

Black-and-white.

Rows of barracks, which once housed hundreds of prisoners, now displayed exhibits about the conditions, stories by the few survivors and newspaper articles from the period.

162

I observed my girls' mouths turn downward as they read the information, and I cried silently for those whose death created this terrible education.

The only thing necessary for the triumph of evil is for good men to do nothing.
Hell on earth.

"Have you noticed something?" I whispered to Fiona, as we perused neighbouring displays. "The word 'killed' isn't used here. It's replaced throughout with 'murdered'."

Moisture formed in her eyes. "It makes it seem less like an event in a war, and more an act of terrorism. Which it was."

We stood, and her hand reached for mine.

A recurring movie showed interviews with elderly people. People who'd survived the holocaust. We watched them tell their subtitled stories.

"These are normal folk." Candi pointed at the screen. "They're not soldiers or fighters." She swallowed. "That lady could be anyone's grandma. Why would Hitler think she was a threat?"

"Did you read the section about how he came to power?" I asked. "He promised the German workers he'd rid them of foreigners who were taking their jobs. But I'm sure no-one realised how permanently he'd dispose of them. He conned an entire nation into thinking his beliefs were legitimate. Only his most deranged followers understood his master plan, his 'final solution'."

Outside the barracks, we gazed through the windows of the bleak huts which had housed the inmates. A path led across the snow-smooth parade ground, and we followed signs to the crematorium.

The Nazis didn't use gas at Dachau, unlike at Auschwitz and other death camps. But they did use ovens.

Ellie read aloud from a sign. We listened, as emotion caused her to stumble over words.

"As long as this crematorium was exclusively in use, the people working here were not permitted to talk about what they saw. When the five or six Jews were completely worn out by this gruesome work, which often continued uninterrupted day and night, their work detail leader simply shot them down on the spot and replaced them with new inmates."

I covered my face with my hands, then wiped them down my cheeks. We stared silently at the chambers. They resembled Tollwood Winter Festival's wood-fired pizza oven, which made this aspect of the killing ground so much more sickening.

Pizza ovens.

Wood-fired pizza ovens.

Wood-fired pizza ovens for cooking people.

We departed via giant memorials built in recent years to commemorate those murdered in this awful place. Protestants, Catholics, Jews, divided by religion, united in death. Our hands clasped in front of us, we stood in silence. The experience reminded me of standing at a war memorial, or in a military graveyard, except these people who'd died weren't military. They weren't combatants.

They were civilians.

They were people like us.

They were us.

We walked slowly to our car, not saying a word.

Fiona opened the boot. "Oh, no. I forgot to bring the picnic. I must've left it at the hostel."

"I'm not hungry," said Candi. Her shoulders drooped.

"I don't feel like anything," said Ellie.

"Me neither." I opened the car door.

We left the silence of the birds and drove away from the death camp.

I cleared my throat. "What were your impressions, girls?"

"I learnt so much," said Ellie. "About the politics, and the history leading up to the holocaust, as well as,"—she paused and sucked in—"as well as what happened here."

"I'm glad we came," said Candi. "It's a horrible experience, but our generation needs to see it. Thank you for bringing us."

My eyes teared up again, and a lump formed in my throat.

"What are we going to do this evening, to cheer ourselves up?" I asked, as we rested on our bunks. I chopped a pinched-from-breakfast apple into quarters and crunched it.

"Let's visit the centre of Munich and see our last European Christmas markets," said Fiona. "We'll be in Scotland tomorrow. And tonight, we could eat dinner in the Hofbräuhaus."

"What's the Hofbräuhaus?" asked Ellie.

"The biggest pub you've ever seen. It sells traditional German food and traditional German beer, and there'll be a traditional Oompah band playing traditional songs."

"Sounds very traditional," said Candi. "Are we allowed to have a beer there?"

"Of course. So long as we're accompanying you. But first,"—I tugged vouchers from my pocket—"we'll claim our free one from the hostel bar."

"Thanks for recommending Tollwood last night," I said to the barman, as we sat in a row on the bar stools holding our drinks like a scene from *Coronation Street*.

"No problem. Did you enjoy it?" He sparkled glasses using an electric machine on the counter which whirred like a dentist's drill.

Fiona nodded. "Yes, especially the Flugelhorns."

"And the pizza," said Candi.

"What's the plan for tonight?" he asked.

"More Christmas markets," said Fiona. "And the Hofbräuhaus. How far is it to walk to the centre of town?"

"Twenty minutes. Turn left out of the hostel and keep going. Which markets d'you want to see? There are several."

I sipped my beer. "Which one's the best?"

"The Christkindlmarkt at Marienplatz attracts the tourists. It's the original market and dates back to the fourteenth century. There are traditional stalls, and a massive nativity scene. And, of course, the glockenspiel."

"The glockenspiel." I smiled and gazed into the distance. "I wanted to hear it last time I stayed in Munich, but I never found myself in the town square at the right time. We must hear the glockenspiel."

"Is there glühwein?" asked Ellie.

"Of course." The barman unfolded a map and laid it on the counter. "There are other markets in the streets around the Marienplatz. There's the Viktualienmarkt, full of food and drink to sample."

"I like the sound of that," said Candi.

"There's the Eiszauber, where you can ice skate."

"Erm, I think we'll skip skating," I said. "Especially after glühwein. I don't want to break an arm."

"The Christmas Village at the Residenz, the city palace, is beautiful, too. But for a unique experience, I'll tell you about somewhere most tourists don't see."

165

He leant towards us, lowered his voice conspiratorially, and we crowded in to hear him.

"In the back streets, there's a tiny Christmas market." He held his thumb and forefinger slightly open to show how tiny it was, then tapped his map. "Here, on the Briennerstrasse." He paused, and we hung on his words. "The Munich Medieval Market. You won't have seen anything like it anywhere else."

Kylie directed us towards the Marienplatz; the central town square with its ancient buildings and intricate glockenspiel. Early evening gloom had settled on the streets and Christmas lights twinkled in every shopfront. Smoke rose from a stall vending caramelised nuts, a product that in my not-insubstantial experience always smelt better than it tasted.

We paused at a pedestrian crossing, where police officers surrounded a young man sitting in the middle of the road.

"Has he had an accident?" asked Fiona.

The lights changed in our favour, and we strolled across the road towards the action.

"You know what this is?" I said, sneering. "It's a protest. I've seen events of this type on the news. The bloody idiot's glued himself to the tarmac."

We approached the scene and stared at the youth. He sat upright with his hands stuck behind him and ignored the police officers. Several similarly aged people waved banners displaying a slogan we couldn't translate.

"He's so lucky," said Ellie, as we walked past.

"Lucky?" I asked. "Why is he lucky? He'll have to be unglued somehow, and he'll be arrested and taken to the police station."

She looked around at the banners. "I don't know what these guys are protesting about, but they're allowed to wave their banners and glue themselves to roads. Think of the people in Dachau. They couldn't do this. They had no rights. All they could do is be worked to death." She jabbed her finger at the superglued youth. "That's why he's lucky."

I slumped and hung my head, as I realised the deep impact our morning's visit had made.

How quickly we forget.

166

How quickly modern life provides distractions which allow us to forget.
How easily the events of Dachau could happen again.
"Thank you, Ellie," I said. "Thank you for reminding us."
The only thing necessary for evil to triumph in the world is that good men do nothing.
I squeezed her shoulder. "Um, goodness knows how they'll unstick him."

The path opened into a wide, pedestrianised shopping street, which had the propensity to be fatal to my wallet. Shoppers hurried past carrying armfuls of carriers, and an enterprising glühwein stall serviced people's thirst before they reached the main Marienplatz market.

Fiona stared through a shop window. "My goodness. Look at these coats. How warm would they be?"

A white, puffy cocoon enveloped the mannequin in the display. The coat reached down to its ankles and was topped in a wrap-around hood which encircled its face, so all we could see were eyes and nose.

"I want one," said Fiona.

"Really?" My eyebrows raised.

"Yes. I'm going to try it on."

"It's massive." I inspected the coat. "How would you fit it in your suitcase? And you couldn't wear it on the plane; you'd never be able to…"

My words addressed empty air.

22. GLOCKENSPIEL

The shop door closed, and I remained alone on the pavement, which was the normal shopping experience for our family.

I turned the handle, entered the emporium and paused. The scent of expensive perfume stuck to every surface. A Joanna Lumley-type assistant arranged hangers on a rack. She shot a look at me from under her bouffant, blonde hair, and I concluded I was considerably under-dressed for this establishment. Her colleague turned away as I scuttled past. Neither of them asked if they could help me; it was obvious every cashmere jumper, every leather glove, every item within their charge was significantly beyond my budget.

Ellie idly looked in a mirror.

"Where's Mum?" I hissed.

"In the changing room with Candi, trying on the duvet thing."

"Seriously? Does she know how much it costs?"

"I don't think so. Do you?"

"Um, no. But nothing's cheap here. Why couldn't she wait for England and visit Primark? Or Marks and Spencer?"

"I think she's in love with this jacket, Dad." Ellie grinned. "You'd better increase the house loan."

Candi exited the changing room and exchanged knowing looks with us. A white, walking eiderdown followed her.

Ellie giggled. I hid a smile.

"What?" said Fiona's voice from inside the eiderdown. "This is so cosy; I could live in here."

"Mum, you look like a cartoon caterpillar," said Ellie.

"She does, right?" Candi laughed. "The one from *A Bug's Life*."

A tag dangled from the bottom of the perambulating duvet, and I turned it over and gasped. I addressed where I hoped Fiona's ears were.

"This, um, item is almost two thousand euros."

"So?" said the eiderdown, in a muffled version of Fiona's voice. "I'd never need to buy another coat, ever."

"That's what you said with your last coat. And the one before."

"And? I collect coats."

"Could you please not collect this one?"

"It looks stupid on you," said Candi.

"I'm glad you like it, Mum," said Ellie, "but it might be a bit big."

"All right," said Fiona. "I'll put it back."

She returned to the changing room to remove the cocoon. Joanna Lumley ignored us professionally as we departed.

"Damn." I gazed up at the clock tower in the Marienplatz, surrounded by stalls selling the usual Christmas market fayre, and clicked my fingers once. "It's ten past five."

"So?" said Candi. "Did we have a booking or something?"

"No, the glockenspiel on the tower plays at five o'clock with dancing figures, and while Mum was trying on the caterpillar coat, we missed it."

A four-storey Christmas tree and busy market stalls glowed with twinkly lights in the shadow of Munich's 13th century town hall, and I stared up at the famous glockenspiel mechanical clock with its dancing figurines.

"We'll return for the six o'clock chimes," said Fiona.

I puffed. "Provided you don't see any more millionaires' jackets."

"Let's find the medieval market," suggested Ellie, "and return to watch the glockenspiel."

"How far is it?" asked Candi. "I'm hungry."

"You'll have to be hungry for longer. We'll eat at the Hofbrauhaus later."

"Could we buy a snack?"

"Maybe. Let's see what the medieval market sells."

We followed Kylie's directions through the back streets around Munich's Marienplatz, ducked through an arch and arrived at the Munich Medieval Market, held in a small square surrounded by imposing snowy-roofed stone buildings.

"Wow," said Candi. "You could imagine yourself in a street scene from the Middle Ages."

"This part's like the other markets." Ellie pointed. "They have sausages." Steam rose from metal containers dispensing the fragrance of cooked pork.

"Yes, and there's where they come from." I indicated a small pig rotating on a spit.

"Disgusting," she said. "Enough to make me become a vegetarian. Almost."

"If you become a vegetarian," asked Candi, "could I have your sausages?"

"That's how they cooked pigs in the Middle Ages," I said. "It's so easy to be fooled by supermarket presentation, isn't it?"

Wooden stalls surrounded the cobbled square, and peasants and nobles strolled amongst visitors dressed in clothes from the 2020s. Some peasants smelt authentically pungent. The juxtaposition of ancient and modern made me feel like a *Star Trek* character who's been transported back in time four hundred years.

We unearthed some suitably modern hot chips and picked at them as we strolled.

In the far corner of the market, we came across a display which freaked us out more than the roast pig. A window featured a selection of animated puppets, which could've been characters from *Grimms' Fairy Tales*. Ogres, wizards, elves and dwarfs gyrated awkwardly and brandished assorted instruments. In the centre stood a fairy, which had been obviously fashioned from a discarded Bratz doll.

"Weird." Fiona stepped back from the window. "Creepy."

"Like something from a horror movie," said Ellie. She looked away.

Candi nodded. "Yeah, the Stephen King one with the clowns."

"All right," said Fiona, "let's look at nicer toys. There's a Steiff shop across the road."

Ellie furrowed her brow. "What's a Steiff shop?"

"The most expensive, cuddly teddy bears you'll have ever seen."

"More expensive than the caterpillar coat?" I asked.

"Yes, but not as warm."

"Look," I said, as I picked up a stuffed tiger and ran my hands through its opulent fur. "All the teddies have the Steiff button in their ear to show they're genuine."

Candi snuggled a toy polar bear the size of a Labrador. "Dad, can I have this? It's so fluffy."

"Don't be ridiculous. We're not here to buy anything. Besides"—I looked at the label—"it's eight thousand euros."

"Eight thousand euros?" said Ellie. "How can a teddy cost eight thousand euros? Are there any normal-priced teddies here?"

"Why don't you two wander around and see if you can find the most expensive teddy here, and the cheapest?"

"If I find the most expensive one, can we buy it?" asked Candi.

"No."

The girls perused the aisles. Ellie discovered a lion worth thirty thousand euros, and Candi successfully won the low-price competition by unearthing a tiny teddy attached to a keyring, which cost a mere forty.

We were about to leave when Fiona tapped my shoulder and pointed. "Look, Simon. A cuddly capybara."

"Seriously?" I rushed over to the brown, furry, snub-nosed toy and held it up. "I have to buy this."

"It's the same size as the polar bear," said Candi. "Mum'll never allow you to have it."

Fiona twisted the price tag. "Six thousand euros. You'll have to be content with taking a photo."

I squeezed the capybara teddy, posed for Fiona's phone, then replaced it alongside its colleagues on the shelf.

"Maybe I'll find one in a cheaper shop."

"Dad," said Ellie. "It's after six o'clock."

"So?"

"We've missed the glockenspiel again while we were looking at teddies."

"Damn. Okay, who's hungry?"

"Me," said Candi.

"I could eat something," said Fiona.

"Shall we walk to the Hofbrauhaus, eat dinner and experience the glockenspiel on the way back to the hostel?"

We marched between rows of long benches populating the cathedral-like interior of the Hofbrauhaus, an establishment which had supplied beer to the population of Munich since 1589. I'd last visited in 1995, and the smell of the beer hall transported me back to my twenties, drinking the local brew, singing the German traditional songs and making best friends with everyone.

"There are no free tables. It's full." I enviously watched tourists and locals swigging from the one-litre glass-handled jugs known as steins. Other groups patrolled the hall searching for seats, and we became contestants in a game with no rules.

A server in traditional Bavarian dress pushed past me, six steins brandished in her hands.

"We should've booked," said Ellie.

"I'm not sure you can book. I think it's first-come-first-served."

"Dad." Candi pointed. "At the back. They're opening another section."

My mind performed a quick time-and-motion calculation. Had our competitors noticed the new area, and could we reach it before they did, without betraying our intentions?

I nonchalantly strode towards the newly cleared tables pretending I was looking for the toilet. We lolloped at a gait fast enough to reach them before others, and slow enough not to be obvious. Several groups spotted our cunning plan, and we competed with them in a last minute-dash.

"Good spot, Candi," I said, as I slid into a seat, tugged off my jacket, leant forward on my folded arms and smiled. Within seconds, every table in the section had filled.

Fiona picked up the menu. "What beers do they sell here?"

"Hofbrau. That's all. This is the Hofbrauhaus. The House of Hofbrau."

"Oh. Do they serve other drinks?"

"I'm not sure. It's a beer hall. Not a vineyard."

Fiona flipped the menu over and inspected the back page as if she expected an extensive cocktail menu to jump out at her.

"Could we order now?" asked Candi.

"Yep," said Ellie. "I want to drink an entire stein of beer and see what effect it has on me. Purely as a scientific experiment, you understand."

"Um, maybe start with a half-size stein?" I suggested. "It's almost one pint of beer, which is more than enough for a seventeen-year-old who's not used to it."

"Are you ordering a whole stein, Dad?" asked Candi.

Fiona rolled her eyes. "Of course he is."

Candi checked her phone. "Could I borrow your beer and take a photo of myself with it?"

"I see. You don't want to drink the beer. You want to impress your friends in Australia that, while they live somewhere where they're not allowed to drink any alcohol until they're eighteen, you're in Germany downing a beer the size of a rainwater tank?"

"Yep. Hurry up and order, Dad. Snapchat's waiting."

A Fraulein (waitress) brandished a pen and pad at the end of our table. She could've been the daughter of the jolly, plump lady who'd served breakfast.

I ran my finger down the menu. "Um, hello. Two half steins of Hofbrau, one whole stein of Hofbrau, and, Fiona, what would you like?"

Fiona turned to the Fraulein. "Do you serve other drinks?"

"We have wine," said the server. "And soft drinks."

"Do you have lemonade?"

"Ja."

"Could I have beer mixed with lemonade?" asked Fiona.

"Okay." She wrote on a pad, swivelled and walked away.

"This is among the best beer in the world," I whispered. "Why are you diluting it with lemonade?"

"You know I can't drink neat beer. I'm having a shandy."

I rolled my eyes. "A shandy. In the Hofbrauhaus."

"Dad," said Candi from behind the menu. "They don't serve chips."

"Of course they don't. This is the Hofbrauhaus. It serves traditional Bavarian food and traditional Bavarian beer. Which doesn't include chips."

"I'll have the Original Hofbrau sausage platter," said Ellie.

Candi licked her lips. "Could I order the whole, roast, suckling pig?"

"Jeez." I thumped the table. "No, you can't order an entire pig. You'll never finish it."

"Aw. Okay, I'll have the Hofbrau fried sausage. What's sauerkraut?"

"Pickled cabbage."

"Lovely. The Germans know how to make food attractive, don't they?"

"As I've said before, great beer; not-so-great food. I'll have the sausage too. What are you eating, Fiona?"

She flipped the menu over and back. "Are you all ordering sausage?"

"This is the Hofbrauhaus. Home of sausages, roast pigs and boiled beef."

"I'll have a small mixed salad. It's the only fresh greens on the menu."

The Fraulein dumped one large stein and three half steins on the table, and I dictated our food order. Another lady, also decked out in traditional Bavarian dress, drifted past holding a basket of giant pretzels, so I flagged her down and bought one to share.

As the food arrived, an Oompah band struck up traditional Bavarian songs, and diners swung their steins in the air and sung along. We joined them, singing in pidgin German.

"Bavarian food's stodgy, isn't it?" shouted Fiona above the singing. "I'm glad I ordered salad."

"Yes," I yelled back. "You need the stodge to soak up the beer. It goes down easily."

"It does, doesn't it?" said Ellie, brandishing her empty stein.

"Did you drink an entire half stein of beer?" asked Fiona.

"Yes," said Ellie. "Could I order another one?"

"No, you cannot."

Candi belched Homer Simpson-style and passed Ellie her glass. "Finish mine. I've decided I'm not a big beer drinker." She stared at her phone and took a picture of herself.

"Thanks," said Ellie. She swigged from half-stein number two, and we all joined in with the chorus.

Four drinks, three sausages and a salad later, we were ready to leave.

"It's half past seven," said Fiona. "We've missed the seven o'clock glockenspiel."

"We can peruse the market stalls while we wait for the eight o'clock one," I said, slipping an arm into my coat.

"Dad, I think I'm drunk," said Ellie.

"I'm not surprised."

Ellie grabbed Candi's shoulder. "Could I hang on to you? I can't walk straight."

The Oompah music deafened us as we circumnavigated the band's pedestal and exited through the throngs of happy, singing drinkers. Cold, fresh air slapped our cheeks as we departed. Ellie grasped her sister.

Fiona turned to Candi. "This is the first time you've helped your sister home after a few beers. I'm sure it won't be the last."

Candi grinned. "What makes you think it's the first?"

"The glockenspiel's in twenty minutes." I hurried to enter the Marienplatz. "This is a magnificent spot to watch it from. All these figures come out and dance, and…"

"I'm not going to make it to eight o'clock," said Ellie. "I need the toilet right now. I'm busting."

She grabbed Candi's arm and towed her towards the hostel, and I resigned myself to never hearing the glockenspiel.

My low-tech alarm clock played an annoyingly joyful melody.

"Time to get up," I shouted at the sleeping inmates of Bavarian Cell Block H. "We need to leave by 7:15 for the Edinburgh flight."

I switched on the light.

"Turn it off," yelled Candi's duvet. "We'll catch the next plane."

I poked her. "We can't. EasyJet run one flight per week on this route. If we miss it, you'll be living in this dungeon for another seven nights. Pack your bags, hop downstairs and hope the nice German lady has kept her promise and laid out breakfast early."

"My head hurts," said the lump in Ellie's bed.

"Your big day," I said. "Time to meet your fellow Scottish redheads."

"My fellow Scottish redheads won't have drunk as much beer as I have."

"Up," I said, pulling at her covers. "Up. Now."

We tumbled down to breakfast at 6:45.

"Half an hour to eat and leave," said Fiona. "Stop stressing, Simon. We've plenty of time."

The dining area stood in darkness.

"Where's breakfast?" asked Candi. "I'm starving."

I tapped my watch and huffed. "More to the point, we've a plane to catch. Where's that helpful server? She promised she'd have breakfast ready early for us."

A light shone from the food preparation area at the rear of the dining hall, and I poked my head around the entrance.

"Guten Morgen," I said to a bottom protruding from a cold store. "Could we have breakfast now? We have to catch a plane."

A woman closed the fridge and stood. Tall and skinny, with a sharp, pointy nose, she was the exact antithesis of the plump, jolly Bavarian lady we'd seen the previous morning.

"Breakfast is at seven," she said. "Not before."

23. PRESENT

The lady's closely cropped bleached-blond hair spiked like a hedgehog who's received a nasty electric shock. She placed a large milk bottle down on a worktop.

"But we need to catch a plane. Please?" I made a praying motion. "We told the lady yesterday."

She shrugged. "That is your problem. I am not the lady yesterday. Breakfast is at seven."

She switched on the dining room lights and began to trickle coffee beans into a machine. Possibly one by one.

Fiona grabbed my arm. "Sit down. We'll delay her if we stand and watch."

The lady brought out plates and trays and laid them on the counter, leaving each covered with a thin cloth.

I watched her take each slow, deliberate step and clenched my fists. "I swear she's taking longer to annoy us."

Fiona pushed me down into my seat. "We'll eat breakfast quickly."

"I'm starving," said Candi.

"My head hurts," said Ellie.

I poised on the edge of the chair like Usain Bolt preparing for the starter's pistol.

The lady continued to set out ingredients.

At 6:57, I stood, and she glared at me, so I sat again.

False start. Too quick off the blocks. Reset.

7:00 a.m.

She whipped the cloths from the food, and we raced towards the dishes like seagulls headed for an abandoned picnic.

I willed the coffee machine to drip faster. "Don't spend ages selecting things," I yelled over my shoulder. "Grab anything, quick. Fill your pockets for later."

Fiona hovered above the bread counter. "I'm not giving myself indigestion. We have two hours until the flight leaves."

"Yes, but it takes forty-five minutes to drive to the airport." I slapped my forehead. "And I forgot to fill the car with petrol. They'll charge us a fortune if we return it empty. Hurry."

Ellie spooned fresh fruit into her bowl. Candi grabbed a packet of Coco Pops. I stuffed one croissant in my mouth and placed two on my plate.

Fiona contemplated the toaster.

"You don't have time to toast it." I waved my arms. "Spread butter and jam on cold bread." I stuffed my second croissant in.

She set her jaw. "I'm having toast. Shut up and eat your pastries."

"Okay. But swallow quickly." I finished my third croissant before Fiona sat down, folded my arms and stared at everybody else while they ate.

Ellie peeled the top off a yoghurt pot and scooped it over her fruit.

Fiona cut her toast in half.

Candi stuffed in cereal, belched and stood.

"You're not having seconds, are you?" I glared at her.

"Of course. How often do I have the chance to eat two free portions of Coco Pops?"

"It's 7:10. We're leaving by 7:15. Even if you haven't finished your second bowl."

I watched Fiona eat tiny bites. "You're not planning on cooking more toast, are you?"

"No. I might grab an apple for the car."

I pushed my chair in as everybody shovelled their last mouthfuls.

"7:15. Well done. Grab your bags and run for it."

Candi held her stomach. "I feel sick."

I tapped my foot in front of the car park pay station, which had clearly been programmed to take longer to process your ticket if it assessed you were running late. Car engines echoed, and tyres screeched as vehicles circled up and down the ramps behind us.

The machine swallowed my ticket, spat it back at me and displayed text under a circle containing a red exclamation mark.

I turned to my family. "What does 'Nicht gültig für den Wiedereintritt' mean?"

Candi shrugged. "You're the one who's supposed to understand German."

"Use Google Translate," said Ellie.

I typed in the phrase. "It means 'Not valid for re-entry'. Strange. The hostel man said this was free parking."

"Maybe you're allowed one free entry and exit?" suggested Fiona. "When we drove to Dachau yesterday, perhaps we used our free one?"

"Great." I banged the front of the machine. "How do we leave the car park?"

"You'll have to visit the window on the ground floor and ask the man there."

"Bloody hell. We're never going to make this flight. Could you pack the bags in the car while I run downstairs?"

I jumped down the eight flights of concrete stairs two at a time and threw open the door at the bottom. An old man sat in a kiosk wearing a workman's jacket and a beanie hat.

"Bitte (please)." I tapped on his window and waved my little rectangular piece of cardboard at him. "Es gibt ein Problem mit dem Ticket. (There is a problem with the ticket)."

He cupped one hand to his left ear and leant forward, and at that point I knew we'd miss the plane.

"Simon, stop racing around the car park. You're making me sick." Fiona grabbed the handle above the passenger door with one hand and the edge of my headrest with the other.

179

A Capybara for Christmas

"I can't believe I had to buy an extra ticket from a man who not only spoke no English but also didn't seem to understand any German." I accelerated down a ramp. "This one had better work at the barrier."

"Dad. The barrier. It's here. Stop!" Ellie shouted from the back seat, as the red-and-white car park arm threatened to slice our Peugeot's roof off.

I inserted the ticket. "Fingers crossed."

We waited.

The message on the screen changed to something in German I couldn't translate.

The barrier didn't open.

"Now what do we do?" I unclipped my seatbelt. "I'm going to force the barrier up and drive under it."

"You can't," said Candi. "Criminal damage. You'll be arrested."

"Press the red button," said Fiona. "Under the ticket slot."

I pushed it and heard a ringing tone.

Come on, come on.

"Ja, kann ich ihnen helfen? (Yes, may I help you?)" answered a woman's voice.

"Das Ticket funktioniert nicht (The ticket won't work)."

Silence. Crackly German.

"Das bloody ticket doesn't work," I said, louder.

"Don't swear at her," said Fiona.

More crackly German.

"This is ridiculous." I thumped the steering wheel. "We're so late."

"Dad." Candi tapped my shoulder. "The barrier's lifting."

I looked ahead, saw my exit was unobstructed, stamped on the accelerator and shot forward.

"Turn right," said Kylie, reassuringly, as I paused at the exit to the main road.

"I hope it's one of those no-speed-limit autobahns to the airport." I pushed the accelerator and nipped around a bus. "We'll need to drive at three hundred kilometres per hour to make up time."

"Slow down," said Fiona, as I changed lanes between trucks. "You shouldn't drive this fast when it's snowing."

"We can't slow down. We'll miss the plane." I gripped the wheel and stared into the weather.

"If we crash, we'll definitely miss it."

"Don't forget we need petrol," said Ellie, from the back seat.

180

I shook my head. "No time now. We'll have to pay whatever they ask at car rental returns. Everyone, look out for the airport sign."

"There," said Candi. She pointed to a blue overhead sign with a symbol of an aeroplane.

We followed a perimeter road for miles on a comprehensive tour around most of Munich airport, then entered an underground car park. A man wearing a black Enterprise Car Hire-logoed jacket guided us into a bay.

"Grab the bags," I said. "I'll deal with this chap."

"Hello, Herr Prior," said the man. He inspected the vehicle and tapped on an iPad. "My name is Henrik. When you fill in your customer survey, please be sure to say I have given you excellent service."

"Yes, sure. I'll put whatever you want. Please be quick. Our flight leaves in an hour."

Henrik sat in the driver's seat and pressed the Peugeot's ignition button. "Herr Prior, you are supposed to return the car full of petrol."

"I know. We couldn't find a petrol station. How much is it?" I tugged wads of cash from my wallet. "I can pay now. Hurry."

He smiled at my panic.

"Herr Prior," he said. "As it is Christmas, I will give you a full tank as a present. Enjoy your flight and thank you for choosing Enterprise Car Hire."

"Thank you so much." I exhaled and gave him two thumbs-up. "Is that everything?"

"Yes. And please mention my name in the customer survey."

"Of course. Five stars. Thank you. Oh, and happy Christmas."

I ran after my family, and we raced for check in.

And if anyone needs to rent a car in Germany, I can recommend Enterprise Car Hire. Especially Henrik. He's great.

"Made it." I sagged against a pillar and panted, as we joined the rear of the check-in queue for the Edinburgh flight.

Ellie surveyed the passengers. "Where are all the Scottish redheads? Where are my people?"

"Maybe these are Germans travelling to Scotland, rather than Scots returning home?" said Candi.

"There's a bald man with a red beard." Fiona nodded her head to the left. "I'm sure he had red hair before he lost it."

"There'll be redheads everywhere in Edinburgh," I said. "Don't worry. You'll meet your tribe."

We checked in and headed to security, where a sign advised us that passengers with an electronic chip in their passport could pass through automatic gates. Barriers whirred open and closed as travellers scanned their documents.

"I love these machines," I said. "Quicker than queuing for an agent."

"And they don't ask you hard questions," said Fiona.

I inserted my document's photo page, faced the camera and marched through the immigration gates.

"You're next," said Fiona to Candi. Ellie continued to scan the room, searching for Robert the Bruce-lookalikes.

Candi turned to her mother. "I can't use this machine as I'm under eighteen. It says I must see an agent."

"Where are the agents?" I called over the barrier.

Fiona asked an airport employee, who held an arm towards a side corridor.

"I'll meet you at the gate," I shouted, as my family disappeared, and I strode into the departures lounge.

"Good morning, Ladies and Gentlemen," said an announcer with a Scottish accent reminiscent of *The Krankies*. "EasyJet flight EZY6912 to Edinburgh is now ready for boarding. May I invite any families with small children and those passengers who require extra time to step forward?"

A couple with two toddlers and an elderly man using a walking stick stood and collected their possessions.

I hovered, glanced over my shoulder in the direction of passport control and chewed my nails.

"Thank you, Ladies and Gentlemen," said Wee Jimmy Krankie. "May I now invite passengers seated in rows one to fifteen to come forward? If your row number is sixteen or above, please remain seated for now."

I inspected my boarding pass. 24E.

The line dwindled, and Master Krankie continued. "Thank you for your patience, Ladies and Gentlemen. Could all passengers for flight EZY6912 please present themselves at gate forty-nine?"

Travellers stood, gathered their belongings and approached the gate.

No sign of Fiona, or the girls.

I sidestepped the queue and spoke with the orange-jacketed EasyJet staff member. "Excuse me. My family's stuck in immigration. They'll be here soon."

"The doors close in five minutes. Can you call them? Maybe they're lost in the airport?"

She turned away and continued inspecting the boarding passes of passengers who'd successfully navigated spiky-haired breakfast ladies, unforgiving car parks and petrol station-less freeways.

I tugged out my phone. None of my family had an international SIM card. They all relied on me to hotspot them. How would I contact them?

Candi. She always finds free wifi.

I opened Messenger and typed.

>>> Where are you? The plane's about to leave.

SEND

I stared at the screen and willed letters to appear.

No response.

Nothing.

More nothing.

I typed again.

>>>Hurry. The flight's closing.

The last passengers entered the air bridge, and the EasyJet staff member turned to me. "Any sign of them? We're about to close the doors."

24. MINCE PIES

I glanced at my phone and saw something I never thought I'd be so pleased to read.

>>>*Candi is typing…*

Come on.
Hurry.

>>>*Candi is typing…*

The staff member looked at me expectantly.

PING
>>> *Coming. Two minutes.*

Yes!

I showed my phone to the lady. "They're on their way. Please hold the plane. Please don't take off without us."

At the far end of the long corridor leading to immigration, I saw a group of three people sprinting towards me. One had Ellie's distinctive red hair.

"What happened to you?" I asked, as they arrived, panting, and Fiona tugged out her boarding pass. "I nearly flew to Scotland by myself."

"There was a massive queue for passport control. A flight from India and another from America landed before us, and we lined up behind all of them."

"It's a good job the queue moved fast enough," I said, as we strode down the air bridge.

"It didn't. We weren't going to make it."

"Um, so how come you're here?"

"Mum did a sneaky," said Ellie.

I rolled my eyes. Fiona's 'sneakies' with immigration terrified me. I imagined my family locked in an interrogation room, being questioned by Kojak-like border agents, as had happened to me years before at Auckland airport.

Candi grinned. "She slipped us through the other queue."

"What other queue?"

"The one for European nationals. There was nobody in it, 'cos they use the electronic gates, like you did."

"And they allowed you through?"

"The lady gave me a funny look," said Fiona, "stamped our passports and said, 'Thanks for the geography lesson. I didn't know Australia was in Europe.'"

I grinned and shook my head. "I wouldn't have the guts. You're amazing."

A London-style taxi whisked us through Edinburgh's granite streets, bordered by dark, stone-fronted, imposing buildings. The sun shone from a pale-blue sky, and people strolled in light jumpers and shirts, four days out from Christmas.

"Where have all the fairy lights gone?" Ellie grasped the taxi's dimpled handhold and stared from the window. "Europe had so many Christmas decorations, but there's none here. I'm not sure country twenty-three's as good as I thought it'd be."

"Scotland doesn't celebrate Christmas so ostentatiously," said Fiona. "Their main party night's New Year's Eve, which they call Hogmanay. Dad and I stayed here for Hogmanay before you were born."

"A night I won't forget in a hurry," I said. "When you drank all those Kahlua shots and tried to kiss a policeman and—"

"Ssh, Simon." Fiona dipped her chin. "The girls don't need to know."

"What?" asked Candi. "Tell us, Dad. Don't leave us in suspense."

"What happens at Hogmanay stays at Hogmanay," said Fiona. She gave us a hard stare.

"And where are the redheads?" asked Ellie, staring out of the taxi window. "I haven't seen a single one. And nobody's wearing a kilt or playing bagpipes."

"Thank goodness," I said. "I hate the bloody racket. So, what's Scotland famous for, girls, apart from Hogmanay, redheads and bagpipes?"

"It's part of the United Kingdom," said Candi, "but it has its own parliament, which is a devolved unicameral legislature with fifty-nine MPs, headed by the First Minister Nicola Sturgeon."

"Have you found free wifi and read that on Wikipedia?"

"No, Dad. I studied it in politics."

The taxi entered the city centre, wound through narrow, one-way streets, and dropped us outside a small apartment hotel. As our accommodation wasn't ready yet, we abandoned our bags at reception.

"I'm starving," said Candi.

"Okay, what does everyone want for lunch?"

"There's a Starbucks over there." Fiona pointed. "I haven't had Starbucks coffee since I last visited the UK. It's one of my holiday goals."

"Starbucks. Are you kidding? We've flown to Scotland for coffee in an American multinational fast-food joint?"

"Starbucks is my favourite. It's Christmas, and I demand my gingerbread latte."

The short, broad lady serving in Starbucks had bright-purple hair, much to Ellie's disgust.

Fiona ordered drinks and a cake for all of us.

"A hyne-a hoony goon noonety," said the lady.

"Pardon?" Fiona shrugged.

The lady repeated her request louder, as Fiona was obviously deaf.

"A HYNE-A HOONY GOON NOONETY."

Fiona shook her head. "Sorry. I'm a visitor here."

"Canna hoot ye doota?" inquired the purple-haired one, throwing her hands in the air. At this point, I employed my usual foreign-country-payment technique and emptied my pockets onto the counter. The lady muttered to herself and selected coins and notes.

We sat at a table which clearly hadn't been cleaned since the cafe had been built. I stuck my tongue out, grabbed one hundred napkins from the counter and swept the detritus of the previous diners' meals onto the floor.

"Yuck. This place is filthy," I said, as my shoe peeled off the floor and unstuck from spilt coffee. "Why don't the staff clean the tables? Why do I have to wipe it?"

"This is weird," said Ellie, quietly. "Scotland's like England, with the same money and the same car number plates I remember from last time, but with an almost unintelligible accent. I found the Germans easier to understand."

"It's a good job we're in Edinburgh and not the Highlands," I said. "You would've been more linguistically challenged there."

We consumed what I considered to be ridiculously expensive, sugary-sweet, playtime coffee and cakes and discussed our plans.

"Tomorrow," advised Fiona, "we're visiting Holyrood Palace in the morning. After lunch, we'll walk the Royal Mile up to Edinburgh Castle, and at 3:00 p.m, I've booked us on a tour about life in Edinburgh during the Black Death."

I pushed my plate away. "This cake tastes like it was made during the Black Death."

Fiona ignored me. "The day after, we'll visit the Royal Yacht Britannia, before heading south to England and Rob and Marie's for Christmas."

"Holyrood Palace? Royal Mile? Edinburgh Castle? Royal Yacht?" Candi ticked on her fingers. "Is everything here connected to the Queen?"

"The King, now," said Fiona. "We must become accustomed to saying King Charles."

Candi rolled her eyes. "Where are we going this evening? Balmoral?"

"Let's buy groceries, explore the centre of Edinburgh, head back to the apartment and make dinner," suggested Fiona. "I can't wait to shop in Marks & Spencer's food hall."

"Marks & Spencer?" asked Candi. Her eyes lit up. "Do they have the same shops in Scotland as in England?"

"Yep," I said. "The whole of the UK has the same chain stores."

"Primark?" asked Ellie and Candi simultaneously.

"Um, yes, I'm sure there's a Primark here."

"I need some new bras," said Candi.

"I need new sports gear," said Ellie.

Fiona raised one finger. "And don't forget, we must buy dresses for your school formal." She turned to me. "It sounds like we're clothes shopping tonight."

My shoulders slumped. "I had hoped we might make it to England before this began. We've been in Britain forty minutes, and the world's greatest shopping expedition's started already." I pursed my lips. "Although, could we visit a bookshop? I finished my capybara owner's guide on the plane. And, devastatingly, I've concluded it's not possible to keep one as a pet in Australia."

"You're seeing the capybara for real in less than a week. Can't you wait until then? The zoo's bound to have a gift shop which sells animal books."

"Why is my shopping less important than yours?"

Fiona ignored me and finished her gingerbread latte. "That was heavenly." She removed the lid and scooped brown, sticky sludge from the bottom of the cup with a spoon. "Everybody done? Simon, can you ask Google where the nearest Marks & Spencer is, please?"

I sighed and addressed my phone.

"Turn right and cross Waverley Bridge," instructed Kylie, the sole female in our party not intent on visiting emporiums of wardrobe-clogging items and aimlessly feeling hundreds of garments. Dusk came early in these far-north latitudes, and lights shone from every store as Christmas shoppers weaved and dodged around each other.

Candi pointed. "Look, a Christmas market. I thought you said the Scots didn't focus on Christmas."

We inspected a sign at the market entrance.

"Glühwein for six pounds?" said Fiona. She blew out her cheeks. "Twice the price of Germany."

"I think," I said, "this is a market for people who've never seen real ones. A Disneyland Christmas market."

"You pay to enter," said Ellie, pointing at a man in a kiosk. "It's not authentic at all."

"Turn left onto Princes Street," said a muffled Kylie from my pocket.

"I can't believe how many people jaywalk here," said Candi. "That girl strolled in front of a bus, looking at her phone."

188

"You're looking at your phone," said Fiona.

"Yes, but I'm not walking in front of a bus."

We traversed Princes Street without looking at our phones or being run over by buses and passed all the familiar British stores.

"You have arrived," confirmed Kylie, as we entered Fiona's haven of shopping wonder, a branch of which she hadn't attended for eight years.

Marks & Spencer.

Scottish shoppers navigated around our stationary tourist-shaped barrier as we paused in the centre of the ground floor and gazed. 'Frosty the Snowman' played from ceiling speakers, and a smell of cinnamon floated through the store.

"Yuck," said Candi. "These clothes are disgusting."

"Um, is this how you remember it, Mum?" asked Ellie.

I stared, wide-eyed. "I think, Fiona, you're the youngest shopper here by forty years. These clothes look like they'd suit your grandmother."

Fiona stood with her hands on her hips and rotated her gaze across the racks of flowery tops, dresses with puffy sleeves and outfits resembling those worn by Amish ladies in the *Witness* movie. "Shall we head to the bra department, girls?"

During any clothes shopping activity, my role comprises seven steps, which must be observed in the correct order:

1. Wait outside the fitting rooms.
2. Don't say "I'm bored," or, "How much longer will this take?"
3. Exclaim how nice every garment looks on my wife.
4. Don't complain when we leave the shop having bought nothing.
5. Repeat at the next shop.
6. Carry bags in the unlikely event of a successful purchase.
7. Don't express surprise when said purchase is returned for a refund the following day.

In my opinion, the best kinds of ladies' clothes' shops were those which provided a men's creche of comfortable chairs near the fitting rooms. I perched on a mannequin's plinth in Marks & Spencer's bra department, scrolled on my phone and searched Amazon for another capybara book. Two other men also hovered and, although we experienced identical tedium, in the best British tradition we gazed in opposite directions and ignored each other.

"I miss Marks & Spencer now we live in Australia," said Fiona, as she exited the fitting room for the eighth time and donated most of the shop's lingerie department to me for safekeeping. "The bras are so comfortable."

After an hour of underwear shopping, we rode the escalators down to Marks & Spencer's basement emporium of fine foods, which I found considerably more entertaining.

Candi shoved a box of Christmas mince pies, a packet of luxury shortbread and a Terry's Chocolate Orange into my basket.

I puffed and shook my head at her. "Where's the fresh food?"

"What, Dad?" she said. "We need food for Christmas."

"We're at Rob and Marie's in England for Christmas."

"Exactly. These snacks are to take to their house."

"But will the snacks last that long?"

"You're right," said Candi, plopping in another chocolate orange, "I'll buy snacks for now, and snacks for Christmas Day."

"I haven't seen a single redhead," said Ellie. The corners of her mouth turned down. "I thought there'd be so many in Scotland."

"Maybe we'll see some tomorrow," said Fiona. "They might be at the Palace, or the Castle."

"Palace? Castle?" Candi paused while grabbing more snacks. "I'm in a *Barbie* movie."

The following morning, crisp Scottish air stung our cheeks as we queued for the Palace of Holyrood House under a white pre-Christmas blanket of cloud. A gentle breeze danced a Walkers crisp packet along the roadway, then it spun into the air and vanished.

I pointed at a road sign and laughed. "We have to post a picture of this. How can there honestly be a street called 'Horse Wynd'?"

Fiona rolled her eyes. "Trust you to find that funny."

"Don't you?"

"It's a Dad joke," said Ellie.

"Here's another one," I said. "This Palace is actually brand-new."

Candi rolled her eyes. "Go on, Dad, why?"

"The building was started in 11-28." I looked at my watch. "It's only 9:30 now. Oh, wait. That joke works better in the afternoon."

Ellie shook her head. "No more Dad jokes, okay?"

"All right. I'm trying to brighten up your day."

"Look, Ellie." Fiona pointed as the queue progressed. "The lady checking tickets has red hair."

"It's dyed," said Ellie.

"How can you tell?"

"It's all exactly the same colour. She's not Scottish, either. She sounds Russian."

The guide requested our tickets in an Eastern European accent and showed us where to collect headsets and controllers with little screens for a self-guided tour. Fiona spent a significant amount of time configuring hers before asking the girls for help.

"Mum, it's easy," said Candi. "You press the number when you want to listen to something. The sign says number one for the courtyard, so if you press '1', you hear about this area."

The rest of us completed number one and continued.

"Hang on," yelled Fiona, extremely loudly. An elderly couple turned around and stared at her.

"Ssh." I glanced around. "You're shouting."

Fiona tore off her headphones. "The volume's too high. I'll be deaf by the end."

"Give them to me," said Candi. She rotated a knob on the side of the device and handed them back.

"Ready, everyone?" I said. "On to number two?"

"Wait," said Fiona. "I haven't done number one yet."

I sighed and realised the entire morning would continue in this fashion.

As we watched highlights on the small screens dangling around our necks, we learnt King James IV had built the Palace of Holyrood House adjoining a twelfth-century abbey. The tour took us through state apartments filled with four-poster beds, faded tapestries and gigantic, gold-framed paintings of former monarchs seated on horses. Its most famous resident was Mary, Queen of Scots, and much of the commentary focused on her imprisonment in the tower and her gruesomely detailed death by execution. I glanced at Fiona and wondered whether my teenagers should have chosen the children's audio option, which might have omitted the gorier elements.

"What did you think of the tour, girls?" I asked, as we returned our equipment and strolled to the exit. I hoped they weren't too scarred by the royal capital punishment; the historical equivalent of King Charles dealing with his paedophile-befriending brother and memoir-publishing son.

"Interesting," said Ellie. "Just like Einstein, in those days, everyone married their cousins and, if a king or queen didn't like someone, they chopped off their head. Even if they were also a king or queen."

"I loved the tour," said Fiona. "I enjoy the history in Britain. There's nothing like this in Australia."

"That's a good job," said Candi. "I don't want my head chopped off."

"Lunch?" I asked, as we trudged up the Royal Mile, passing souvenir shops offering black-and-white terrier fridge magnets, bagpiper dolls and red-and-green tartan shortbread tins. "We should eat something Scottish, to keep our custom of always eating the local cuisine."

"I've already arranged it." Fiona grinned at me. "D'you remember, when we lived in New Zealand in the nineties, we visited a city called Dunedin, which means 'Edinburgh' in Scottish?"

"Of course. Where I drove up the steepest street in the world."

"And, at the time, you mentioned you were so hungry, you could eat a certain type of traditional Scottish food?"

"Did I? Was it Scotch eggs? Shortbread, maybe?"

"Nope. I've booked us into an eaterie called the Haggis Box. How d'you feel about eating a haggis?"

"Haggis?" Ellie poked out her tongue. "Made with sheeps' stomachs?"

Candi puffed out her cheeks. "Ellie, did you have to mention that?"

"Let's at least try it," said Fiona. "We might enjoy it and ask for seconds."

25. WHISKY SAUCE

We climbed steps to the small, glass-fronted Haggis Box café, and Fiona held the door open. A tall man with a generous, black beard stood behind the counter and nodded benevolently over the proceedings.

"Hello," said Fiona. "We've a booking for four people."

He scratched his head. "Booking, hey? Take a seat wherever ye can find one. Grab a menu, and I'll send the wee lad to take ye orders."

We picked up four laminated, A5-sized menus and plopped down on plastic chairs at a bare, Formica table. I hesitated and glanced towards the kitchen. The odour wafting in our direction smelt like Sunday roast lamb, and I hoped this experience might turn out to be pleasurable.

Candi flipped the menu over. "The back's the same as the front. There's one thing on the menu. Haggis."

"Um, yes." I rubbed my hand across my mouth. "This is called the Haggis Box."

"I know, but I thought they might've sold a pie or something."

"You can choose traditional haggis, or vegan haggis." Fiona read from the menu. "And there's an option of whisky sauce or red wine gravy."

"Great," said Candi. "There's haggis with sauce, or for really adventurous diners, haggis with sauce."

"I'll have the traditional haggis with whisky sauce," I said. "See if I can *stomach* it."

Ellie rolled her eyes. "You and your Dad jokes. I'll have the same. We won't find anything more Scottish than haggis with whisky."

"I'll try the vegan one," said Fiona.

"That's not really haggis, is it?" Candi snorted. "Pretend haggis for the squeamish."

194

The 'wee lad', who turned out to be a dark-haired teenager over six feet tall, arrived with a pad and pen.

"Three traditional haggises, please, and one vegan one." I looked up at him. "All with whisky sauce."

"Drinks?" asked the teenager.

"Water for the table, please."

He returned with a jug of water and four glasses. A microwave pinged, and our meals followed.

I inspected the haggis from all angles. "It resembles a Christmas pudding."

"You don't like Christmas pudding," said Fiona.

"What's the orange bit underneath?" asked Ellie.

I lifted the edge of the haggis with my fork. "Mashed turnip, I reckon. The menu said it comes with neeps and tatties. That's Scottish for turnips and potatoes."

"What does turnip taste like?"

"We don't eat it in Australia. It's similar to swede."

"What does swede taste like?"

"Um, pumpkin?"

I tested some haggis. "The whisky sauce is nice. Conceals the haggis taste well."

"You're not selling it to me," said Ellie. She tried a small mouthful.

"How's your vegan one, Fiona?"

"Nice. Want to swap for some of yours?"

"I will," said Candi. "In fact, could I give you mine?"

"You have to eat it," said Ellie to her sister. "I'll make you."

Through superhuman effort, Fiona and I completed our haggises.

Ellie paused halfway. "Sorry, it's, um, too much for me."

I glanced at Candi, who'd eaten a quarter of her portion. "Are you okay? You look green."

"Did we bring the Terry's Chocolate Oranges? I need an emergency one to take the taste away."

Fiona closed the door of the restaurant as we left. "Verdict?"

"I'm glad I tried it," said Ellie.

I sucked in a breath. "I think I'll manage to live the rest of my life without eating another."

"I'm hungry," said Candi.

Fiona laughed. "You should've finished your haggis."

"Where to now?" I asked.

Fiona looked at her watch. "We're early for our next appointment."

"Great," I said. "My turn to do Dad shopping. I need another capybara book." I tugged my phone from my pocket. "Okay, Google, nearest bookshop."

I glanced up, as in the distance I heard a familiar sound which resembled multiple tom cats negotiating a territorial dispute.

"Oh, no," I said. "The traditional bagpiper. Could we turn around?"

"What, back to the haggis café?" asked Candi. "No, thanks."

"C'mon," said Ellie. "I want to see if he has red hair and a kilt." She tugged us towards the cacophony, and my hopes of supplementing my capybara library evaporated.

Disappointingly, the bagpiper didn't have red hair or a kilt. He stood at the side of the Royal Mile wearing jeans and a donkey jacket. We watched him briefly, then left before the caterwauling forced me to snatch his instrument, snap it into pieces, stamp on it and set it alight.

"Here we are," said Fiona, after a short walk. "Our next attraction. Mary King's Close."

"Is this another Royal Palace?" asked Candi.

"It does have the word 'King' in it," said Ellie.

"Actually,"—Fiona assumed a voice like Boris Karloff's *Frankenstein*—"it's about the Black Death. Mwah-hah-hah-hah."

"Nice," said Candi. "We've experienced people having their heads chopped off, lunch made from sheep's bowels and now the plague. What a great holiday."

While the girls explored the gift shop's keyrings, bumper stickers and bone china mugs, Fiona and I queued to show our pre-booked tickets.

Ellie tapped my shoulder. "Look, Dad, it's a teddy black death." She brandished a black, fluffy sausage at me with a price tag of £9.99.

I recoiled. "What the hell? What is it?"

"It's a cuddly microbe," said Candi, holding it to her cheek. "Could I buy it?"

"I can't imagine why any adult would buy their child a toy microbe. This place is weird already."

The lady behind the counter was dressed in brown, filthy rags, and several of her teeth had been blacked out with a marker pen. Behind the fake boils and matted hair, she was probably an attractive university student.

"Welcome to The Real Mary King's Close," she cackled in a Wicked Witch of the West-voice. "May I see your tickets, please?"

This seemed an unlikely request from someone who was clearly in the final stages of multiple nasty diseases, but Fiona complied, and we followed other guests into a small holding area. The lights dimmed, and a video began about the history of Edinburgh during the plague and, more specifically, this warren of underground houses we were about to enter.

"Now what?" I whispered, as the video ended, and the lights remained off.

"Dad, it's scary," said Ellie. She grabbed my arm.

BANG

We jumped, as a pair of wooden panels to our left burst open, and a tall, bearded man entered dramatically.

"Sorry aboot that," he said, in a Billy Connolly lilt. "I did'na mean to scare ye."

He surveyed his charges and grinned. The same costumier had supplied his medieval rags, but the marker pen must have expired as his teeth shone 2020s dentist-advert quality.

We held onto each other and wondered what would happen next.

"You're about to enter a warren of underground dwellings known as The Real Mary King's Close," continued Billy Connolly. "We'll travel back in time through the centuries and walk the lives of people who lived here. And"—he opened his eyes wide—"died here."

"Oh great," whispered Candi. "More head chopping."

The guide continued. "We'll meet Doctor George Rae, who tended the afflicted in the Great Plague of 1645, Walter King, who removed corpses and cleansed the victims' homes, and Agnes Chambers, a maid in 1535, who'll tell us a tale of drama and murder."

"I like the way he rolls the 'r' in murder," whispered Ellie to Candi.

I bent my head to Fiona. "D'you think this is suitable for the girls?"

"They're seventeen. They'll love it. You're more scared than they are."

"Follow me," said the guide, "into the underworld." He returned rapidly through the cupboard he'd burst from, and we tailed him.

Over the next hour, we descended multiple levels, ducking our heads through low, wooden-beamed rooms and scuffing our feet on uneven, mud floors. At various points through the attraction, mannequins covered in pus-running boils greeted us, propped in unnatural positions. Ellie's eyes watered at a realistic montage depicting a lady who'd lost all her children to the plague and was about to succumb to it herself. The guide maintained his jolly Billy Connolly act throughout, which rather offset the sobriety of the history lesson.

The tour ended in the gift shop, and we breathed fresh, un-microbed, lovely, 21st century oxygen.

"What did you think, girls?" I asked.

"Sad," said Ellie. "We're so lucky these days, with modern medicine and clean air. The poor lady whose children all died."

"Did you find it scary? I did. The man covered with black marks who was hours from death, he scared me the most."

"That wasn't who scared me," said Candi. "The plague doctor, with his pointy mask and cloak and stick, he's terrifying. If I had the black death and he came to my house, I'd climb out of bed and run away."

"Maybe that's how he cured people?" suggested Ellie.

"Is there any chance," I asked, "the rest of the day could be less gruesome?"

"Sure," said Fiona. "Would you mind if we returned to Marks & Spencer? I didn't buy enough bras."

My arms sagged by my sides. "I think I preferred the underground plague rooms."

"It's good we booked through a cheap website," I said, as we arrived at the car rental company the following morning to collect the vehicle that would convey us across the border to England. "The list prices are ridiculous. I booked a compact car; I'm certain it won't be big enough. With luck, they'll upgrade us to that Volvo." I pointed at a brand-new, shiny, blue vehicle.

"Or the Audi," said Fiona, indicating its neighbour. "I hope they have an automatic. I'm hopeless with manuals."

We'd left the girls uploading photos at the hotel, while we strolled the short distance to Edinburgh railway station, where the car hire company's offices were based down several flights of concrete, urine-scented stairs on a basement floor of a car park.

"Good morning," said the car rental lady. "Do you have a reservation?"

"We do," I said. I handed her the paperwork and our driving licences.

"Are you both driving?"

"If possible."

I waited with my hands in my pockets as the clicks of her keyboard echoed around the office.

She glanced up from her screen. "Your booking allows one driver. You're welcome to add another, but it'll cost four hundred pounds extra."

"Four hundred pounds?" My mouth fell open.

"It's twenty-five pounds per day. You rented for sixteen days."

Fiona leant on the counter. "Could one of us drive for the first eight days, and the other for the second?"

"No. Not unless you pay the four hundred pounds."

"But that's ridiculous." I folded my arms. "Only one of us can drive at a time."

"Sorry. Company policy."

Fiona held my shoulder. "You drove all around Europe; I'll drive here. I'm not wasting four hundred pounds of good shopping money." She turned to the car rental lady. "Just me driving." She smiled shyly. "We hoped you might upgrade us. Maybe to the Audi?"

"Or the Volvo." I wondered if Fiona's vehicle ambitions might be going too far. "We seem to have bought more shopping than a compact car will contain."

The lady studied her screen but didn't smile. She tapped her keyboard. "We could upgrade you to the Audi"—Fiona grinned and clenched her fists in front of her—"for an extra fee."

"How much of an extra fee?"

The lady tapped her computer again. "Three thousand pounds."

"Three thousand pounds?" My eyes opened as wide as tractor tyres. "Three thousand pounds? We're renting the car, not buying it."

"It's Christmas," explained the lady.

"I'm well aware it's Christmas. How much is the Volvo?"

She sighed and tapped some more. "Two thousand pounds extra."

"Far out." Fiona shook her head. "We'll take whatever we booked online."

The lady tugged a set of keys from a ziplock bag, and we followed her into the parking area.

"Here's your car," she said. She opened the door of a minuscule Vauxhall, which smelt of mould and didn't appear to have been driven in months. Possibly years.

I inspected the car, unlatched the boot and peered in.

"Um, this seems rather, er, tiny? D'you have anything bigger?"

"Sorry. You booked a compact car."

Fiona slumped into the driving seat.

She turned the key and a slow, coughing sound emitted from the exhaust. "At least it starts."

I tapped the car's information system. "It doesn't have Android Auto. We can't connect Kylie."

Fiona swung the wheel, released the handbrake, and we drove up the ramp to the next level. She craned her neck left and right. "Where's the exit?"

"Next level up, I think." I studied the rental car information. "This piece of paper says the barrier code's 1374."

We lurched around another corner and ascended another ramp.

"There." I pointed. "The arrow says 'exit'."

Fiona spun around the final corner, headed towards the barrier and applied the brakes.

A grinding noise sounded from the rear wheels, and the car continued its progression towards the barrier.

"Simon!" shouted Fiona. "The car won't stop. Help!"

200

26. CAKE

I yanked the handbrake, and the car stalled.

"I'm not driving this any further." Fiona opened the driver's door. "How can they rent a car which doesn't have working brakes?"

"We can't leave it here. This is the exit from a public car park. Reverse slowly, and I'll stop it again."

"Are you sure about this?"

"Do we have a choice?"

Fiona reversed, and I tugged the handbrake.

"Now drive carefully in first gear. Don't press the accelerator. Let it creep forward. I'll pull on the brake if needed."

"Um, okay."

Fiona edged down the ramp. I pulled on the handle once we'd reached the bottom, and she steered to the left. We repeated this complicated two-person manoeuvre four times and halted outside the rental office, accompanied by a noticeable burning smell.

I threw open the car door and marched to the counter. "The car you've rented us; the brakes don't work. It could've killed us."

A man exited the back office. "I'm the manager," he said. "What's the problem?"

"This car"—I jabbed my finger accusingly at the Vauxhall, which steamed where Fiona had left the engine running—"the brakes make a horrid grinding sound. I had to pull on the handbrake to stop us crashing into the barrier. Clearly nobody's checked whether this car's roadworthy."

The manager didn't seem too concerned, and I concluded this wasn't the first time one of his vehicles had attempted to assassinate a customer before reaching the street.

"Leave it there," he said. "We'll find you another one."

I began to inquire how he'd achieve this, as his employee had stated every car was reserved, but Fiona winked at me and held one finger vertically over her lips.

The manager scrolled through his iPad. "We do have another car, but it's an automatic. Will it be okay?"

Fiona grinned briefly, then her expression changed to a frown.

"It'll have to do," she said.

I heard a silent 'woo-hoo' in her response.

"And," he said, "it's slightly larger. I hope you don't mind."

"I suppose we'll tolerate it," I said, with another silent 'woo-hoo'.

"Great," said the manager. "I'll fetch the keys. And if you have any more problems, here's my card. Call me directly."

Two minutes later, we pressed 1374 and exited the car park in the brand-new Volvo.

"Where've you been?" asked Ellie, as I dashed into the hotel reception. "You took ages fetching the car."

"I know, and now we're late for our Royal Yacht appointment. Grab the bags. Mum's parked outside."

"Wow," said Candi, as she climbed into the back seat. "I love the new car smell."

"Two thousand miles on the clock," said Fiona. "Will this suffice to take us to England?"

"I reckon so," said Ellie.

"Turn right, then, turn left," added Kylie comfortably from her brand-new, unscratched, Android Auto display, and we headed for Edinburgh docks.

The salt air of the Firth of Forth permeated through the air, and seagulls' cries echoed overhead as we collected the inevitable headsets and entered a world of teak walls, brass light fittings and rotary dial telephones.

"At least this attraction won't involve anyone dying or being dismembered," said Candi.

I pressed 'start' on my device. "You hope."

We followed the electronic guide's prompts through the five decks, beginning at the upper state rooms, working our way down through the officers' quarters, below again to where the ratings slept and ate and finishing well below the waterline where the engineers worked. The yacht had been trimmed for Christmas; at the end of the vast state dining table, a huge gold, red and green wreath decorated the wall. Fiona plucked a menu from a place setting.

"Are you supposed to touch?" I asked. I glanced around, but no black-jacketed guide stood in the corner.

"I'm studying the food they ate. Jugged hare? Grouse? I wonder whether Prince Philip shot those before they boarded."

"Very probably. Put it back."

A better depiction of the British class system could not have been designed. As we descended the steep steps, the beds became smaller, the dining facilities became less ostentatious, the ceilings became lower, and bare, metal floors replaced the shag-pile carpet.

"I noticed something," said Ellie, as we convened in the gift shop following our tour. "Everybody slept in a single bed. Even the Queen. How egalitarian."

"She must've preferred it," I said. "Although not everyone ate and drank the same way. What about the gigantic oak table for state dinners, compared to the cramped mess where the sailors took their meals?"

"What I found most interesting," said Candi, "was how divers checked under the boat for bombs every day."

"I loved it," said Fiona. "I wish I'd been a maid when the royal family was on board. They would've overheard some juicy gossip about what the royals thought of other people."

I patted her shoulder. "Even before Meghan Markle arrived on the scene."

"Next stop, England," said Fiona, as we climbed back into the car. "Could you ask Kylie to take us to the Lake District, please?"

"Okay, Google." I addressed the phone and informed Kylie of our next destination.

"This route contains roadworks," she stated, as if they were an allergy-causing product in a Christmas cake.

"Avoid roadworks," I instructed.

"Avoiding roadworks," confirmed Kylie, in the style of the computer on *Blake's Seven*.

"She's so clever, isn't she?" I clapped. "I remember holidays with my parents; we'd spend hours stuck in traffic somewhere on the A303 in Somerset, with the car threatening to overheat, and my father becoming more and more grumpy. I wish we'd had Kylie then."

Fifteen minutes later, we sailed out of Edinburgh onto a dual carriageway.

"Told you," I said with a thumbs-up. "We haven't spent a moment stuck in roadworks."

"Turn left," advised Kylie.

"Um, I don't feel we should leave the main road." Fiona slowed and indicated. "It doesn't feel right."

"Kylie's still diverting us around traffic." I patted the display twice. "She'll find the quickest route."

We followed her instructions and headed down a smaller road.

Drizzle began with occasional heavier showers.

"Could we eat lunch now?" asked Candi. "It's one o'clock."

"Did we bring lunch?" I asked.

"Yep," said Fiona. "Marks and Spencer quiche, scotch eggs and shortbread."

"Great," said Ellie. "Another car picnic."

Candi puffed. "At least it's not haggis again."

"All right," I said. "We'll stop in the next layby."

The drizzle intensified, and Fiona switched the windscreen wipers to full.

"Turn right," instructed Kylie joyfully, in a voice more suited to a blue sky, sunny, Bondi Beach day.

"I'm not sure this is the correct route," said Fiona. She cornered, and we immediately climbed a steep, winding country lane bordered with high, dry-stone walls.

"When's the next layby?" asked Candi.

"How should I know?" I said.

"I'm hungry."

"I know. So am I."

An occasional farmhouse materialised through the mist, and Fiona peered ahead and hooted as we approached each blind bend, but we didn't see another vehicle, or any humans.

"I'm stopping." She swung the Volvo into the entrance of a field. Multiple sheep who hadn't seen a car in months congregated on the opposite side of a gate and baahd excitedly at our arrival.

"You can't park here," said Candi. "This is a farmer's entrance."

Fiona switched off the ignition. "If the farmer comes, I'll move. Open the boot and take the picnic out, Simon."

"Why me? It's tipping down."

"You're nearer."

I forced the door into the wind and stepped out. It immediately blew shut, and the horizontal rain stung my face. I wiped my cheeks and opened the rear hatch, which provided brief shelter. Memories of family holidays flooded back.

For some reason, each summer, my father elected to drive the length of Britain in his Austin Allegro, a vehicle model so unreliable, it should never have been allowed to exist. As we proceeded along windy country lanes, inevitably at least three things would happen:

1. The car would overheat, break down or suffer from a flat tyre, and my mechanically challenged parent would trudge to a nearby farmhouse and impose on the occupant to assist a poor traveller in distress.

2. We would be lost. I'm convinced we always booked the most remote accommodation, at the end of an unmarked track, in a village which, for some reason, had a nearly identical name to several other villages in the neighbourhood.

3. We would eat in the car. Always. The steam from a Thermos flask would fog up the windows, as my mother produced Tupperware of every shape and size from a wicker hamper and passed cheese sandwiches to the back seat, cut into quarters so they lasted one bite before I needed another one.

I closed the boot and realised I'd become my father.

"Here." I dumped the picnic on Fiona's lap and crashed back into the car. "Could you start the engine and turn the heating on? I'm soaked."

"We can't run the engine while we're stationary," said Ellie. "It's bad for the environment."

"Sod the bloody environment. Not running it's bad for me. ACHOO."

We sat and ate our picnic. No cars passed, and no farmers visited the sheep.

"This definitely wasn't the quickest way," said Fiona after lunch. The sky lightened, and we drove into a long, winding river valley.

"Isn't this prettier than the motorway? We're experiencing remote parts of Scotland most tourists wouldn't see."

"Most humans wouldn't see," said Candi. "We've passed one car in the last hour."

"Turn left," advised Kylie, and after a further right and a left, we rejoined main roads, speeding vehicles and civilisation.

"This is far less attractive," I said, as a passing truck threw water across our windscreen.

Fiona pointed. "We must show this to the girls." She swung the car off the road again and entered a car park.

"Where are we?" asked Candi.

"Gretna Green. This is where young English couples ran away to be married. It's the first town across the border into Scotland, and Scottish laws allowed them to marry at sixteen without their parents' permission. They still hold weddings here today."

Fiona pointed at a horse and carriage, upon which a soggy bride and groom sat and smiled for photographs.

"I'm seventeen," said Candi. "I could legally be married here."

"You'd need a boyfriend first," said Ellie. She stared, opened the car door and stepped out.

"Where are you going, Ellie?" called Fiona. "D'you need the toilet?"

"Nope. I've spotted something. Everyone, come with me." She marched away, and we shrugged at each other and followed her.

27. CHRISTMAS DINNER

The drizzle paused and, in the late afternoon gloom of a Scottish day, we discovered what had attracted Ellie's attention. Beside the horse and carriage holding the drenched bride and groom stood a bagpiper, playing 'The Wedding March'.

Ellie photographed him with her phone.

I draped my arm around her shoulder. "You finally discovered a proper one with a kilt," I said. "And he has red hair. It doesn't make the music sound any better."

"Yep," said Ellie. "I've found one of my people." She took a deep breath and savoured the moment.

We stood and listened to the bagpiper until he finished squeezing the life from the wild cockerels he clearly kept in his tartan-coloured pipe-sack, then visited Gretna Green's gift shop and toilets.

"It's almost dark," said Fiona. "We should leave. We still have over an hour until we reach Rob and Marie's."

We didn't discover exactly where we crossed the English border and left country number twenty-three behind. Night fell, and we swept along pitch-black roads into the Lake District as headlights blinded us approaching through the rain.

"So," said Fiona, "That was our European holiday. We added six countries to your tally. Ellie achieved her goal of finding a red-haired bagpipe player. You girls both drank glühwein at Christmas markets. We all enjoyed shopping."

"You might've enjoyed it," I grumbled. "I didn't."

Fiona ignored me. "There's two holiday goals we need to tick off before we start thinking about the Japanese leg of our trip." She patted my leg. "You and your capybara animal encounter."

"That's more important than a holiday goal." I nodded. "A life goal. A bucket-list item."

"And," said Fiona, "a good, British curry from a good, British, Indian restaurant. I'd be happy with one for Christmas dinner."

"We can't tell Marie we want a curry. She'll have prepared a huge turkey with stuffing, roast potatoes; Brussels sprouts."

"Oh, yes," said Ellie. "I can't wait."

"Knowing her, she'll have remembered we enjoy her homemade Yorkshire puddings too."

"I'm hungry already," said Candi.

"I love Marie's cooking," said Fiona, "but if she told me we were having takeaway curry tonight, I wouldn't complain."

"You have arrived," confirmed Kylie, as the Volvo's headlights lit up our friend Marie, standing in her driveway, wearing a kitchen apron. The rain paused, and the tarmac shone glossy reflections.

Fiona switched off the engine. We swung open the car doors and took it in turns to hug and kiss our host.

I stood back, frowned and tilted my head. "What's wrong, Marie? Is everything okay?"

"I'm so annoyed with myself." She wrung her hands. "I know you all like my home cooking, and I spent ages in the kitchen today, but"—she appeared to be about to burst into tears—"I've had a kitchen disaster. Everything's gone wrong. I'm so sorry."

Fiona rubbed Marie's upper arm. "Please don't be upset. We weren't expecting anything extravagant the day before Christmas Eve. We'll be fine with a sandwich."

Marie wiped her eyes, smiled and shook her head. "Oh, no," she said, in her soft, Cumbrian accent. "No guests of mine'll be eating sandwiches. I've sent Rob out to buy a takeaway curry. I hope you don't mind."

She led us into their house, and Fiona took my arm and grinned.

28. DISASTER

Four days later, and 300 miles south

Metal ground against crockery as I stirred my coffee for the twentieth time. We sat around the table of our farmhouse accommodation west of Bristol and recovered from the long motorway journey after Christmas with our friends in the Lake District. The wonderful promise of crisp, streaky bacon percolated from a kitchen behind us where our plump, jolly, farmer's wife host prepared breakfast.

"I hardly slept last night." Fiona rubbed her eyes. "You woke me five times with your farts."

"I can't help it," I said, crossing my arms over my chest. "It's the Christmas food: Brussels sprouts, bread sauce, roast vegetables. Marie entertained us so well. And the puddings." I leant back in my chair and patted my stomach.

"Christmas is weird in the northern hemisphere," said Ellie. "In Australia, we'd have had friends around for a barbecue, then we might've played cricket on the beach or swum in the sea. Here, we ate enough to feed Africa, and then all you adults fell asleep in front of the television. You missed half the day."

"Tell me about it," I said. "Why did I polish off five desserts? I'll need to buy new jeans."

"Great," said Fiona. "You won't complain about today's shopping expedition if we're purchasing clothes for you as well."

"Today's shopping expedition?" I furrowed my brow. "We're clothes shopping today?"

"Of course. Boxing Day sales."

209

"Boxing Day was yesterday."

"They continue more than twenty-four hours, Simon." She rubbed her hands together. "An entire day at the mall. I can't think of anything I'd rather do."

"I can't think of anything I rather wouldn't."

"Deal with it, Dad," said Candi. "We need to buy dresses for our school formal. This'll be a massive shopping session."

"How will we carry it all? The suitcases are bursting. We tipped Edinburgh's Marks & Spencer's underwear department into them. And I swear Primark's racks were empty by the time we departed."

"I brought a spare holdall," said Fiona. "And if we fill it, we'll buy another one."

My chin slowly dropped to my chest.

"Cheer up, Dad." Ellie grinned at me. "Tomorrow we're visiting the zoo where you'll tick off your bucket-list item and hand-feed a capybara."

"I know, right?" I looked up and leant forward. "The best Christmas present ever. I'll bet the capybara's definitely as excited about tomorrow's encounter as I am. I've no idea how I'll sleep tonight."

Fiona yawned. "Without farting, preferably."

"All right," I said, slapping the table so hard several items of cutlery briefly became airborne. "Let's book the capybara experience for tomorrow, then head to the shops." I turned to Candi, the only one of us who needed her phone at breakfast. "Could you hop on the Internet and grab the zoo's number?"

My fingers drummed, while Candi typed and scrolled.

She stopped.

She scrolled up again.

She paused.

She scrolled down.

"Dad. There's a problem."

"What kind of problem? Has the entrance fee increased? Is it hard to find the zoo? Is it raining tomorrow? I can deal with any of those."

"This is a bigger issue. The zoo's closed."

"Closed?" I drew my head back. "What d'you mean, the zoo's closed? When I looked a few weeks ago the website said, 'Open all year except Christmas Day'. And today's the 27th of December. Are you sure you're looking at the right zoo?"

"You look. Here." She thrust her phone in my face, and the bright-yellow banner at the top of the screen beamed at me.

Chew Valley Animal Park.

Closed from Christmas Day. Reopening February 1st.

I scrolled up and down on the phone.

I held it away from my face.

I read it again, word by word.

I handed it back to Candi, clasped my hands around the back of my neck and clonked my forehead on the table.

Silence.

Fiona wrapped her arm around my shoulders.

I lifted my head and puffed out my cheeks. "This is a disaster. I'll never meet a capybara now."

PART TWO

29. NATION STATE

The Japan Airlines plane snoozed on the tarmac, an air bridge umbilicaled to its fuselage. A threatening background announcement informed a Mr and Mrs Patel they were inconsiderately delaying other passengers and, if they didn't present themselves immediately at gate four, their flight would depart without them. Candi stretched out and performed the vital function of advising her 9,742 Snapchat friends of her current location at Heathrow Airport, as pilots and cabin crew strolled past the waiting passengers and boarded the plane.

"There are three things I'm looking forward to in Japan." I formed a steeple with my fingers and leant forward. "Eating sushi, singing karaoke and watching sumo wrestling. Anything else will be a bonus."

"I need clothes shopping," said Candi.

"Me, too." Ellie nodded. "I love those white coats with fluffy hoods you see Japanese girls wearing on Instagram."

"The clothes will be my size." Fiona grinned. "Japanese ladies are tiny."

"You shopped so much in England our luggage barely fitted in the rental car." I scratched the back of my head. "How will we lug any more around? In Tokyo, we'll have to manage on public transport."

"We'll find a way." Fiona turned to our daughters. "There's always a technique for carrying more shopping, right, girls?"

"And we must visit a cat café," said Candi.

"Yes!" said Ellie. "Those kitties are so cute. Have you seen them on Facebook Reels, Dad?"

"Cat café?" My eyes opened wide. "What the hell's that?"

Candi brandished a photo at me of a fat tabby. "A café where people drink coffee and pat cats."

"Seriously? You have a cat at home."

"I know, but this is an experience unique to Japan. You wanted to do cultural things."

"Um, okay. At least you both learnt Japanese in primary school. You can translate for us."

Candi puffed. "All I remember is: 'yes', 'good morning', 'thank you' and 'teacher'."

"And 'good evening'," added Ellie.

"Hopefully, everyone speaks English. What else did you learn about Japan at school?"

"It's a nation state," said Candi. "Almost the entire population is the same race."

"Japanese, I presume?"

"Of course. There are barely any immigrants."

"They catch whales under the guise of scientific research." Ellie frowned. "In reality, they're eating them. If we see anywhere serving whale meat, I'll be sick. Apart from that, I can't wait to see Japan." She grasped her boarding pass and grinned. "Country twenty-four."

"How will we know what time zones our bodies should be on?" asked Candi. "My phone automatically updates to local time."

"Remember this?" I cocked my head and tugged my electronic alarm clock from my hand luggage. "Good, old-fashioned low-tech. No wifi. No Bluetooth. Just batteries. We, um, need to be fast asleep right now."

"Useful," said Fiona. "A clock which tells us when we should be asleep, even though we can't be."

"Ladies and Gentlemen." A voice intonated a long paragraph of Japanese, then paused. "Flight JL44 for Tokyo Haneda will depart shortly. May I invite any families with small children to pre-board now by approaching gate seven."

As in many conurbations, more than one airport administers to the giant metropolis of Tokyo. On opposite sides of the city, Haneda and Narita airports balance like two opposing counterweights. Haneda airport thronged with passengers that evening, and we marched along the kilometres of beige carpet between the gate and immigration. Melodic, electronic beeps like the noise emitted by 1980s Casio digital watches preceded lengthy, complicated announcements in the native tongue.

"Did anyone sleep on the plane?" I asked, glancing at the airport signs and drinking in the foreign-ness of a new location.

"Nope, I watched three movies," said Candi.

"I might've had an hour," said Fiona. "Ellie slept on me."

"I didn't," said Ellie. "My eyes were open the entire flight."

"It's late evening now," I said, "so we should be able to sleep straight away. The capsule hotel's in the airport."

"I can't wait to try it," said Fiona. "I've seen them on travel programs. Rows of horizontal pods stacked on top of one another. You climb in, and there's enough room for a mattress and a pillow. It must be Tokyo's way of dealing with overcrowding."

"Yep," said Ellie. "Tokyo's one of the most over-populated cities in the world. Too many humans."

"There'll be four more now," I said. "Does everyone have their QR codes?"

At home, I'd spent six hours filling in forms on my laptop to generate the QR codes required to enter Japan, the strictest post-covid immigration process enforced by any country, maybe except North Korea. Each traveller required three codes: one for border control, one for customs and one for quarantine.

Three codes per person.

Four of us travelling.

Twelve slips of paper, each with a random checkerboard pattern of black-and-white squares.

Three hours to transcribe the information for the first time. Another three when the website crashed and my printer malfunctioned, forcing me to repeat the entire process.

I'd carefully cut out the twelve codes and labelled each with our names.

Japan immigration *couldn't* refuse us entry.

Airline staff flapped laminated cards above their heads, indicating smug people such as us, who'd prepared their QR codes in advance, should head through the right-hand channel. They herded disorganised, unprepared travellers who'd failed to spend six hours at their computers into a chaotic holding area, where they frantically clicked phones and copied information from passports.

I smirked and wielded my printed, square, paper codes at every staff member as we successfully won the contest to reach immigration.

The young, thin border agent bowed slightly.

"Konbanwa (good evening)," I said.

"QR code, please. Blue one." Her dainty fingers reached out.

"Watch, girls," I demonstrated to Candi and Ellie. "The polite way to deliver a document in Japan is two-handed. It demonstrates the importance of the exchange of information and your respect for the recipient."

The agent bowed, accepted my codes, rotated them and showed them back to me. "This is paper?"

"Yes," I replied, in agreement with her extraordinary perspicacity.

"Please show on phone."

"I can't. I typed the information on my computer at home and printed them out."

"We need on phone. Very sorry."

"I don't have on phone. Very sorry." I shoved all the paper QR codes over her counter in a very impolite single-handed gesture.

She raised her hand and summoned a supervisor. They bowed to each other and conversed in their native tongue. At one point, our documents passed delicately between them, and they pointed at them together as if they were kindergarten children sharing a Ladybird book.

The supervisor addressed me. "Vaccination certificates?"

"Yes. We have them."

Fiona slid them from the envelope containing our travel documents. The supervisor bowed, and I copied the action subconsciously.

She briefly inspected them, passed them back to me and spoke again to the first agent, who stamped our passports and waved us through.

At no point during our subsequent meetings with customs and quarantine did anybody ask to see any QR codes again.

"What a waste of time," said Fiona, as we propelled our heavy trolleys into arrivals. "In the end we didn't need any of those bits of paper; just our vaccination certificates."

"That's six hours of my life I'll never get back." I shook my head and puffed.

"But if you hadn't printed them," said Ellie, "we'd still be in the holding area tapping phones."

"Checking in." I addressed the young man behind the airport capsule hotel desk. He bowed, accepted the document with our booking details and handed us four grey, linen bags accompanied by keys and plastic-wrapped paper instructions.

Candi crackled the cellophane open and read the information. "We turn right, Dad, and you turn left. Men and women are separated."

"Oh. I guess it's goodnight. See you in the morning."

I heaved one of our suitcases, pushed a door displaying the internationally recognisable 'gents' symbol and entered a world I hadn't seen since my teenage years at English boarding school.

30. CAPSULES

Japanese men in various stages of undress loitered in front of tall, thin, lockers, as if I'd accidentally invaded the Brave Blossoms' changing room after a particularly energetic rugby game against the New Zealand All Blacks. Harsh, bright lights reflected from the white locker doors. Nobody spoke or even coughed. The hiss of distant showers white-noised in a far room, and the mist of spray deodorants permeated the air.

The men paid me no attention, despite my obvious tourist status. I clutched my grey, linen bag, dumped my suitcase on a central bench and scrutinised my new teammates.

All were aged under thirty with neat haircuts. They discarded suits and smart-casual clothes, hung them in lockers, brushed hair and folded spectacles. A staff member weaved between them, scooping discarded towels and disposable slippers. The men put on identical, grey, thin dressing gowns, and the changing room began to resemble a futuristic dystopian movie set, where actors dressed in indistinguishable space clothes and wandered silently through swooshing doors down hospital-decorated corridors.

A tall, young man with blond hair exited the showers and shattered the homogeneity.

I smiled at him and made a small waving motion with my fingertips. "Hi. D'you speak English?"

"Ah should hope ah do," he said, in an accent reminiscent of Rosco Coltrane from *The Dukes of Hazzard*. "Ah come from Alabama." He gave me a lopsided grin.

"Oh, wow," I said. "Have you recently arrived in Japan? I landed this evening."

"Nope. Been here two months."

He removed his grey robe and tugged on jeans and a T-shirt.

"Two months? What, here? In this capsule hotel?"

"Yep. Cheapest place in town. Twenty-five bucks a night."

"Gosh. Um, how does it work?" I glanced around the clinical area. As if responding to a signal from the mother ship, the futuristic dystopian society evaporated, leaving us two foreigners alone.

"You store your belongings in the locker and change into the robe and slippers in your bag."

I opened the grey, linen carryall the receptionist had handed me, which contained a thin robe sheathed in clear plastic and two slippers, each individually wrapped in clear plastic.

"Then," said the tall American, "you shower through there." He indicated an entrance at the far end of the locker room. One of the grey-dressing-gowned space clones cleaned his teeth in front of a row of several identical white sinks, backed by a wall of matching, pristine mirrors. "They should've given you a washcloth and a few other bits."

I rummaged in the bag and retrieved a disposable toothbrush, wrapped in clear plastic, a flannel, wrapped in clear plastic, and a towel. Also wrapped in clear plastic.

"They like their single use plastic here, don't they?" I held up the toothbrush.

"Yes, sir," said the American. "Wait until you visit a convenience store." He stood. "Once you've used the bathrooms, enter the capsule room." He pointed at a plain, white door, flush with the wall behind us.

The words 'Quiet please. Sleeping.' displayed in English alongside Japanese script.

"You'll find two rows of capsules, one above the other. You climb into yours, pull down the blind and go to sleep. Nothing else to do in there." He laughed.

"Right. Do I take the first vacant one I see?"

"Nope. Show me your key."

I held out the large, brown disc with the number 79 embossed on it.

"The key opens your locker. The number's for your locker and your capsule. They've allocated you an odd number which means you're on the bottom layer. Probably because you're older. You won't have to climb the ladder."

220

I was about to explain at the advanced age of fifty-three, climbing into a top bunk was not beyond my capabilities but, as this friendly stranger was aged about twenty-two himself, I figured I seemed positively elderly. I'm sure he noticed my fingers curl and heard my tone of indignation.

"Right. How kind of them to consider my advanced years. Thanks for your help."

"No problem. Enjoy." He tugged on a puffa jacket, shouldered a small backpack, waved and swung the door out to reception.

The deserted changing room suddenly seemed alien and unfriendly. I found my locker, inserted the key and revealed a space two metres tall and twenty centimetres wide.

How on earth will I squeeze a suitcase full of Marks & Spencer bras into here?

1:00 a.m.

I'd slept for three hours in my Japanese space-cocoon.

The capsule area contained one hundred apertures arranged in two horizontal rows as the American chap had described. Each a metre square by two metres long, each enclosing a sleeping human.

To permit sleep at any time, the pod room remained artificially dim. Faint glows emitted from recesses in the perimeter of the floor, as if we stayed in a fictional cryogenic facility.

In between each of the lower capsule entrances, four rungs led to an upper capsule. And at the bottom of each ladder, an identical pair of slippers.

I'd removed my own slippers and clambered into my capsule. In addition to a mattress, the pod contained a built-in, moulded, plastic shelf not quite big enough to rest a mobile phone on, a light and a single, ceiling-mounted power socket. I'd plugged in my charger and lain my head on the insufficient, coarse pillow. The duvet was the size and thickness of a large towel, and I smiled to myself recalling a scene from *The Hitchhiker's Guide to the Galaxy*. An omnipresent, faint, electrical hum had lulled me to sleep.

And I'd slept for three hours, and now my watch said 1:00 a.m., and I was one hundred percent awake and one hundred percent ready to face a new day.

Shit.

I scrolled through my phone and discovered a message from Candi.

>>> Are you awake?

I sat up.

>>> Yes.

>>> I'm not tired.

>>> Me neither. Are Mum or Ellie up?

>>> I don't know. Their pods aren't near mine.

>>> We must try to sleep. Otherwise, we'll be on the wrong time zone.

>>> I know. I can't.

>>> Put your phone away.

>>> You're looking at yours.

>>> We'll both put them down. Good night.

>>> Night, Dad.

Knowing Candi, she'd scroll through Instagram and Snapchat until dawn.

I lay on my back, lifted my head and stared at the dim orange glow which peeked around the edges of the pod's blind.

Random, middle-of-the-night problems tumbled around in my head.

How excited I'd been about meeting a capybara.

Touching one.

Hugging one.

Hand-feeding one.

I'd no idea when I might have the opportunity again, if ever.

My brain spin-cycle clicked onto my current situation.

Alone.

Separated from my family.

Women on one side, and men on the other, as if we holidayed in a Sikh temple.

I closed my eyes and wondered how I'd manage tomorrow on three hours' sleep.

PING

I awoke suddenly, sat up and bashed my head on the ceiling. My phone pinged. Candi again.

>>> Dad. Where are you?
>>> In bed.
>>> Get up. It's mid-afternoon.
>>> Seriously?
>>> We all overslept except Ellie.
>>> Have you showered?
>>> Yes. We're packed and waiting for you in reception.
>>> Okay. Gimme ten minutes.

I raised the blind and peeked out. The pod room looked identical. Dark, weird and other-worldly, with the ever-present soft, orange light outlining each capsule. The difference was, only one pair of slippers remained.
Mine.

My family waited for me on a low, white, wooden bench in reception.
"Ellie, how come you didn't wake us up?" I asked. "We've missed half the day. More than half."
"I figured you were all jetlagged, so I sat in my pod and did homework. Then, one of the staff tapped outside, bowed a lot and told me we had to leave, so I found Mum and Candi's pods and woke them."
"I've already taken a walk," said Fiona. "The 7-Eleven sells coffee and food."
"I need coffee. And I must find a Japanese SIM card. Let's go."

Plastic crinkled and tore as we filled a carrier bag with discarded food wrappers on a step outside the store. My coffee cup warmed my hands, and I inhaled the espresso-flavoured steam.

"No more car picnics," said Ellie. "Step picnics now." She stared into the 7-Eleven carrier, stuffed with plastic bags, plastic wrap, plastic containers, empty drink bottles and discarded coffee stirrers. "None of this can be recycled here. There are no recycling bins. Could we carry it back to Australia and put it in our home recycling?"

"We're not carting rubbish around the world." I rubbed her shoulder. "Sorry, Ellie. We can't fix Japan's environmental issues single-handedly. Let's grab our cases and find the train station."

Ellie frowned and pushed the bag into a bin.

Four groups of travellers queued for the rail inquiries window. We waited behind them as electronic beeps preceded station announcements, and barriers made rapid clunkety-clunks each time a passenger shoved a ticket through them.

"Which station do we need?" asked Fiona.

"Iriya. It's the closest to tonight's accommodation."

The queue edged forward.

"How far is the journey?"

"Um, hard to calculate. It's this side of Tokyo, so we don't have to cross the city, but I haven't worked out the interchanges yet."

The passengers in front of us discussed a complicated itinerary with the lady behind the counter, involving several hundred bows, drawing on a piece of paper and money changing hands twice.

"We've been waiting almost half an hour," said Fiona, loud enough so the information lady could hear.

"Ssh," said Candi. "You can't speak like that in Japan. It's confrontational. People take offence."

"I'm offended I've had to stand here for ages."

The lady bowed as the previous customers departed, and I mirrored her gesture.

"Four tickets to Iriya station, please." I offered a handful of notes.

"Iriya station?"

"Yes, Iriya station. We're staying there tonight."

She paused, considered my request and bowed. "No Iriya station. Iriya station not here."

31. TAMAGOTCHI

I tilted my head at the information lady. "Um, what d'you mean, Iriya station not here?"

"Iriya station not here. Iriya station other train. This Japan Rail. You take Tokyo Metro." She pointed at a second queue on the opposite side of the concourse.

This was our first experience of the complex, bewildering Tokyo train network, where multiple companies operate disparate train lines which don't connect with each other properly, don't share ticket machines, staff or barriers and don't appear on the same maps, despite being in close proximity and often co-located in the same stations. The fun and games we'd enjoy navigating this transportation spaghetti were, for now, in our future.

"I can't believe," said Ellie, as she leant heavily on her trolley, "we queued for nothing. And now we have to line up again. Is this definitely the right railway? I need my bed."

"Um, it's 3:00 p.m. local time. Don't sleep yet; you'll be on the wrong time zone."

"I'm happy to lie down and sleep right here in the airport. It's all right for you; I've been awake since 4:00 a.m."

The Tokyo Metro ticket man wore a smart, black uniform and a peaked cap reminiscent of Morgan Freeman's in *Driving Miss Daisy*.

I bowed. "Konnichiwa. We want to take the train to Iriya."

He tugged out an A4-size paper map and swivelled it on the countertop.

"Iriya. You go Asakusa line." His finger pointed at a symbol buried deep in a rainbow fettuccine of coloured squiggles.

226

"Um, thank you. Four tickets, please."

His arm straightened horizontally in a universally recognisable invitation and indicated a complicated-looking machine mounted on the wall nearby. I imagined this might be the end of our brief, but congenial, relationship, then he exited his booth, escorted me to the machine, pressed the correct buttons, asked me for Japanese money, inserted it for me and presented me with four small, cardboard tickets as if I'd won first prize in a raffle at an English church fête.

He bowed again, and I realised I was beginning to like Japan very much.

"Where are the train pushers?" asked Ellie, as we assembled on the platform, circled around our luggage. "I want them to shove us onto a train."

"What are they?" I asked.

"People who push you onto crammed trains so they can squish as many passengers on as possible during busy times."

"That doesn't sound particularly pleasant."

I attempted to interpret the overhead electronic board which advertised incoming trains' destinations, then marched to the back of the platform to inspect a wall diagram. The Tokyo subway exuded a sweet, fragrant smell, different to the stale air of the London Underground. I stood in front of the map and ran my fingers across its shiny surface.

"Dad, the train's coming," said Candi.

A row of carriages clattered into the station, the uniformed driver standing at the controls. He bowed to the single station attendant, who returned the gesture but didn't see fit to shove anyone anywhere.

My forehead wrinkled. "Don't get on this train. I can't tell if it's the right one. We mustn't end up in a Tokyo suburb miles from where we need to be."

My map investigation continued.

"I'm sure the speakers played 'Humpty Dumpty' when the doors closed," said Ellie.

"It's a tune to warn people they're closing," said Fiona. "It can't have been Humpty Dumpty."

"The next one's not ours," I said, as a second train thundered in. "Maybe the one after."

We watched people alight and embark, dragging luggage behind them.

"It's definitely 'Humpty Dumpty'," said Ellie, as the rear of the train departed the airport station.

The electronic board flipped to the next destination.

"Oh," I said. "The next train isn't going where we need either."

"I'm boarding it," said Fiona. "We'll be stuck on this platform forever."

"But it might not take us the right way."

The train rumbled into the station, and the attendant and driver repeated their mutual bow.

"I don't care," she said, and pulled her bag through the doors.

"Come on, Dad," said Ellie, as she stepped up after Fiona. "We'll work it out once we're aboard."

Candi slumped in a seat next to her sister.

I glanced up at the electronic display, dragged my bag after them and, to the encore of 'Humpty Dumpty', we set off.

"Are you sure this train's headed the right way?" I asked Fiona, as my eyes flashed across the diagrams above the opposite seats for the eighth time. "The boards show three different maps, and I can't work out how they join up. I can find Haneda airport on this map"—I pointed—"and I can see Iriya Station on the other map, but I can't figure out how the maps connect. And what do these other numbers mean? There are three sets of figures for each station."

Fiona glanced around the train's carriage. "Let's ask someone."

"Who?"

"Anyone. This lady." She disturbed a young woman with AirPods stuffed in her ears. "Excuse me, is this train going to Iriya?"

The lady removed her pods, bowed from the neck, shook her head, but said nothing. I wondered if we mis-pronounced the station's name.

Fiona repeated her request and indicated Iriya on the map, then jabbed her finger twice at the train's floor.

The passenger nodded and said, "Hai, Ningyocho." She bowed a few more times and re-inserted her headphones.

Fiona raised her eyebrows at Ellie.

"'Hai' means 'yes'," she explained.

I inspected the maps further, but still couldn't work out how they joined up. We were the only tourists on the train, and everybody wore face masks. Most of our fellow passengers scrolled on their phones, but some read minuscule, paperback books. I glanced over one man's shoulder as he turned pages back-to-front, and I goggled at the vertical writing. Carriages passed us travelling in the opposite direction, and air blasted through vents.

The train continued, and we still had no idea where it was taking us.

"Dad," said Ellie. "Ningyocho station's on the other map. That's what the lady meant. It's one more stop until we change trains. And I've worked out what the symbols mean. Each station has a letter and a number to identify it. This one is A13, which means station thirteen on the Asakusa line."

"Yes, but it also says T10 and G11, and there's a number '1' on the image next to it and a number '6' on the picture of the train."

"T10 means it's also on the Tōzai line, station ten. G11 means it's station eleven on the Ginza line too. '1' means it's one minute until we reach Ningyocho, so it's one minute until we change. And '6' is the number of our train carriage."

"Um, say all that again, slowly?"

Our train successfully clacked into Ningyocho.

"See," said Fiona. "You're always worrying about nothing."

I addressed my family loudly. "Everyone, time to get off. Grab a bag."

"Stop shouting." Candi swallowed and glanced left and right. "People don't shout in Japan. You're embarrassing."

"I'm not shouting."

"Yes, you are. You're still doing it. Ssh."

One line change and five stops later, the train entered Iriya station. I carefully explained to Fiona how H19 referred to the station number, and the electronic display showed we were in carriage three.

Ellie folded her arms. "I taught you that."

The speakers played 'It's a Long Way to Tipperary' before the doors closed, and the platform attendant bowed to the driver.

"Everybody bows here, don't they?" I said. "I've started doing it back to them."

Candi rolled her eyes. "Yes, but don't do the prayer thing with your hands when you bow. That's how they act in Thailand, not Japan."

"Oops. Sorry."

I successfully inserted my new Japanese SIM and re-awakened Kylie, who didn't ask me for a PUK code and didn't seem to suffer from jet lag.

"Okay, Google. Edo Sakura Ryokan." I hoped I'd pronounced the name of tonight's accommodation correctly.

"Exit the station, then, turn left," she said, sounding ready to catch a wave at Bondi Beach.

I made a thumbs-up at my phone. "I'm so glad to hear your voice again."

The Edo Sakura Ryokan stood in a narrow street behind the station. So narrow that, in the absence of any space for raised pavements, white lines had been daubed on the sides of the road. A cool wind blew as night fell, and I noticed an evening star shining through the thin gap in the buildings.

"Watch out," shouted Ellie. She pulled me, as I strolled into the path of an oncoming cyclist, who managed to swerve, yell and bow simultaneously.

"Remember," said Candi, as we slid open the ryokan's wooden door, "you must remove your shoes and wear the slippers when you enter."

"Konbanwa. Good evening." The receptionist bowed and smiled behind her mask. Her traditional, brown yukata uniform was topped with a matching hat.

"Hello. Prior family, checking in." The floor vanished under our baggage.

The receptionist's first question surprised me. "Come, sit down. Leave your bags. Would you like tea?"

This was different to checking into a European Hilton. Especially the one in Mainz.

"Oh. Thank you."

She invited us to sit on circular, black, wooden stools, and we waited while she exited through a sliding door. Plinky-plinky music sounded from invisible speakers, and small, floodlit plants swayed in a miniature courtyard.

"We didn't have to remove our shoes," whispered Fiona.

"I expect we will upstairs."

The yukata-clad lady reappeared holding a tray containing four tiny, handle-less, white mugs. She placed one in front of each of us, bowed and returned to the reception desk.

I lifted the tiny vessel. "Japanese tea. No milk." I took a slurp. "Refreshing."

We completed check-in formalities while seated at the stools, then the receptionist escorted us via the lift to two fifth-floor adjoining rooms.

She unlocked the first one, held out her arm and invited us to enter. "This," she said, "is where Mum and Dad sleep."

We walked in, and Fiona stomped over the floor and dumped her case.

"Mum." Candi buried her face in her hand. "Take your shoes off. It's offensive to walk on a tatami mat in your shoes."

Fiona removed her shoes and averted her gaze.

The room contained a low table, two chairs with no legs and nothing else. I experimented with wiggling my toes into the spongy mat which covered the entire floor.

"Um, excuse me, where's the bed?" I rubbed my chin.

The receptionist opened a cupboard. "Here." She showed us two thin, folded, single mattresses and a collection of sheets and duvets. "These are your beds, and here are your covers. You can make them yourself, or if you are too tired, we will do it for you."

"We'll make them," said Fiona. She swept her arm around the room. "Where do they go?"

"Anywhere you like. But, this"—the lady pointed to an alcove displaying a Japanese print—"is a shrine. You should not point your feet at your shrine."

"Got it," I said. I tugged the bedding from the cupboard, as the receptionist popped next door to instruct the girls.

Our fifth-floor room's window opened into a clear Tokyo night. Adjacent buildings crammed in with zero space separating them. Occasional, tiny, floodlit, rooftop gardens sprouted from smaller blocks, and laundry hung on minuscule balconies. The hum of traffic sounded from a distant main road. I breathed in deeply and inhaled the exotic essence of the Orient.

"Mmmmmm," came a noise from the bathroom. "Mmm. I love this."

I poked my head around the door and found Fiona sitting on the toilet with her eyes closed and wearing a wide grin.

"What are you so happy about? You weren't that desperate, were you?"

"Mmm. Electric toilet seat."

"Electric toilet seat?"

"Yep. It's pre-warmed. Mmmmmm." Her cheeks turned pink.

After a dinner of 7-Eleven processed items wrapped inside multiple layers of plastic packaging, we lay down.

"This mattress is bloody hard." I groaned and rotated onto my front.

"Stop complaining," said Fiona. "You wanted an authentic experience."

"Yes, but the mattress is an inch thick. I can feel my hips and elbows touching the floor." I stood, which wasn't an easy feat from a one-inch-high bed, and adjusted the covers.

"The locals manage. While you're out of bed, could you shut the window?" Fiona pushed herself up on her elbows.

"What was it Ernest Hemingway said? A marriage is a relationship between a woman who cannot sleep with the window open and a man who cannot sleep with it closed?"

"Please close it, Simon. It's freezing. And I can hear a beeping noise outside."

"I can't."

"It sounds like an electronic device. The Japanese have a lot of toys which beep."

I crossed the room and slid the window closed. "There. Now it's quiet."

My elbow banged through the mattress as I extinguished the bedside light. "Ow. I've no idea how Japanese people sleep on these."

"Simon," said Fiona's voice in the darkness.

"Yes?"

"I still hear beeping."

"I've shut the window."

I heard Fiona sit up. "The sound's not outside. It's in the next room. Someone's playing an electronic game."

"I can't hear anything. I'm going to sleep. Ow, my hip." I turned over, winced and closed my eyes.

Pause.

"Simon?"

"What? Bloody hell; I'd just nodded off."

"The beeping. It's like one of those annoying Tamagotchi games. Maybe it's coming from the next room, or it's in the wall? Could you fetch the receptionist and ask her to investigate?"

"I still can't hear it. You're imagining it."

"Please? I'll never sleep with that noise."

I scraped my bones on the floor and stood again.

The receptionist tailed me into the room and bowed at Fiona under her duvet.

"Hi," said Fiona. "Sorry to bother you, but there's a beeping sound. I thought it might be coming from outside, but we shut the window, and we can still hear it."

I waved dismissively. "You can still hear it. I can't."

Fiona ignored me. "We think someone in the next room's playing an electronic game, or maybe the heating's making noises?"

The lady frowned. "I can hear it."

Fiona glared at me. I read the word 'see?' on her face.

The receptionist crossed the room and squashed her ear against the wall. "You're right. Maybe electronic game." She reversed her body and listened with the other ear.

She frowned, crouched close to the floor and pointed at my hand luggage. "I think noise come from this bag."

32. MISO SOUP

"The noise can't be coming from the bag." I shook my head. "I don't own any electronic games."

"Why don't you take the rucksack out of the room and see if the beeping stops?" suggested Fiona.

"Okay, I will, but it won't be in the bag. You'll find it's coming from the next room."

I carried the hand luggage into the corridor and clutched it to my ear.

Beep beep beep beep

I frowned and unzipped the front compartment.

Beep beep BEEP BEEP BEEP BEEP

The noise became louder as I reached in and tugged out the old-fashioned, low-tech alarm clock which for some reason was advertising non-stop it was definitely breakfast time somewhere in the world.

Sweat prickled on my forehead.

Quick, get rid of it.

I dumped the clock in a bin, concealed it with rubbish and nonchalantly re-entered our room.

"Did the beeping stop?" I asked.

"Yes," said Fiona and the receptionist simultaneously.

"Whoever's making the noise must've gone to sleep." I puffed dismissively and rolled my eyes. "Thank goodness. Sorry to have troubled you."

The receptionist bowed. "Is there anything else, sir? Let me know if noise occurs again."

I nodded towards the wall. "Yes, of course. Thank you."

Fiona gave me an odd look as I collapsed back onto the bed and banged my elbow on the floor.

The next day, I woke feeling like I'd slept on the pavement. "I've no idea how the Japanese sleep on the ground like this." My hand clasped my back, and I groaned. "I turned over every fifteen minutes with sore elbows, shoulders and hips."

Fiona ruffled her hair. "You wanted authentic Japanese accommodation. I slept fine."

"Yes, but you're not as heavy as me."

"I can't wait to sit on the pre-warmed toilet seat." She jumped up, disappeared into the bathroom and made mmm-ing noises.

"Hurry up," I said, dancing from one foot to another and holding my crotch.

"I could stay here all morning. Mmm. Mmmmm."

"Time for breakfast." I knocked on the girls' door and shouted. "And could I use your toilet? Mum's glued to the heated seat."

Ellie poked her head out. "I've been awake since 2:00 a.m. My body's still on the wrong time zone. What does your little alarm clock say?"

"Um, I've lost it. No idea where it is. Perhaps I left it at the capsule hotel. Is Candi up?"

"Yep," said a speaking duvet. "I slept great."

"You don't find these mattresses hard? I do."

"Nope. You must be too old for this."

A staff member dressed in a yukata served us a cutlet of salmon, accompanied by multiple tiny dishes containing miso soup, fish roe, egg, cucumber, seaweed, soybean and rice. The little bowls clinkled as she set down each tray, and I wafted the steam of the soup towards my nose.

"I've never had rice for breakfast," I whispered to Fiona. "This is more like dinner. Yummy, though. I hope she brings coffee."

The lady set a cup in front of me of the capacity prim-and-proper Barbie might've enjoyed at afternoon teatime. She clinked a similarly dolls house-sized jug of milk next to it.

"Um, thanks," I said. I tilted my head towards Fiona. "I'm guessing the Japanese don't drink coffee in the morning like we do."

"Like you do, you mean. By the pint."

"What are we doing today?" asked Candi, as she pushed Ellie's head off her shoulder, where she enjoyed a brief nap.

Holding the little bowl in both hands, I tipped back the dregs of my soup and licked my lips. "So long as we eat sushi, sing karaoke and watch sumo wrestling whilst we're in Japan, I don't care in which order we do them."

"Hang on, Simon." Fiona clacked down her chopsticks. "Those might be your Japanese goals, but we have our own ones. I want to see the fish market, for instance. And though it's winter, I was hoping there'd be cherry blossoms. The weather's warm enough for early blooms. The Imperial Palace has cherry tree gardens."

"Could we visit a cat café first?" Ellie yawned. "Maybe I could curl up on a rug and pretend to be a cat."

"I want to go clothes shopping in a suburb I've heard of called Harajuku." Candi scrolled on her phone. "It's where all the young, trendy Japanese shop."

Fiona broke off a piece of salmon. "The fish market's a popular tourist destination. We'll wander around and choose fresh fish straight off the trawlers."

"Will there be much wandering?" asked Ellie, opening her eyes slightly. "I'm not sure how far I can wander today."

I opened my laptop.

Fiona leant over me. "Search for Toyosu fish market."

I typed and pressed 'enter'. "Got it. The website's in English as well as Japanese."

"How do we travel there?"

I ran my finger across the screen. "We take our local train line to a station called Tsukiji, then somehow join another for Toyosu. But this map's impossible to understand. I can't discover whether we can change trains there or not. It says, 'transfer at ground level'. What does that mean?"

"We'll work out the line change when we reach the station," said Fiona. "We're not in any hurry today."

A techno-pop version of 'Green Green Grass of Home' entertained us as the doors opened and we boarded the train. Air whooshed through an open window at the end of the carriage as we set off, and I amused myself trying to guess which jingle would accompany our departure from succeeding platforms. Although seats were available, I chose to stand, and studied the assorted signs advising passengers of the next destination, which number carriage they rode in and which brand of makeup they should buy. The designs differed from western advertisements; more cartoony, with bold, primary colours. I stared at an illustration of a zoo, with cream-coloured creatures that were clearly supposed to be llamas, and terracotta-coloured creatures that could've been almost anything.

Except they weren't almost anything.

The English script under the Japanese writing said 'Kapibara-san'. The cartoon animals were capybaras.

33. CHERRY BLOSSOM

"Everyone, look." I jabbed my finger at the cartoon, which depicted the happy capybara family bathing in a body of water resembling an English duck pond. "This must be an advertisement for a zoo somewhere around here. We have to find out where it is and visit."

Candi scrolled on her phone, then turned it around and showed me a similar picture to the one in the train. "It's not a zoo, Dad. Kapibara-san's a cartoon character. This advert's for a children's TV series."

"Really?" I turned back to look at the advert, then sat down next to her and slumped in my seat. "I had my hopes up there was a capybara zoo here in Tokyo."

Fiona rubbed my shoulder.

Multiple nursery rhyme door closings later, the train clattered into Tsukiji station.

"Information centre." Fiona approached a small booth where a facemasked lady sheltered behind a Perspex screen. "Hello. Which train do we take for the fish market, please?"

The lady stood, bowed and shook her head. "Sorry. No English."

I blinked rapidly. Here we were, at a busy main railway station, and the information centre employees spoke no English. I typed 'Toyosu Fish Market' on my phone, pressed 'translate to Japanese' and rotated the screen so the lady could read it.

"Ah, Toyosu," she said, brightening briefly. She shook her head and looked at the floor. "Very sorry. Toyosu closed today."

"Closed? This fish market is closed?" asked Fiona, speaking louder than might have been considered polite. "Is there another fish market open?"

"Toyosu closed," repeated the information lady, and I realised we'd exhausted her ability to fulfil our knowledge requirements.

I tugged Fiona's arm. "Let's visit the Imperial Palace and find the cherry blossom gardens."

"Another palace?" asked Candi. "Didn't we traipse around enough of them in Edinburgh?"

We blinked on the pavement like miners who'd ascended from a long underground shift, and I instructed Kylie to direct us to the Imperial Palace.

"Cross the road, then, turn left," she chortled.

Fiona pressed a pedestrian crossing button, and traffic halted as the lights changed in our favour.

"I've heard those birds singing all over Tokyo," she said, staring upwards. "It's such a lovely sound to hear in the city centre. Tweet-tweet, tweet. Tweet-tweet, tweet. I wonder what they look like?"

"Mum," said Candi, "They're not real birds."

"What d'you mean, they're not real birds? I can hear them. They must perch in a tree close by."

"The traffic lights make that sound to tell us it's safe to cross," explained Candi, pointing at the signals. "Instead of the boring 'beep beep beep' we hear at home, they play that tweety noise."

Ellie hung her head. "The birds have all died because humans built this massive city, so they replaced them with fake, electronic birdsong." She shoved her hands into her pockets and trudged to the opposite side.

The Imperial Palace gates stood shuttered.

"This city should be called No-kyo, not Tokyo," said Fiona. "Everything's closed." She approached a man in uniform.

The palace guard's outfit complemented the station attendant's peaked cap, black jacket, matching trousers and shiny shoes. He even sported the regulation white gloves.

His demeanour was significantly more officious.

"When's the palace open?" asked Fiona. "Will it be open tomorrow?"

241

The guard bowed minutely and indicated a sign in Japanese and English.

I read aloud. "The palace is not open to the public except on January 2nd, for the New Year's Greeting, and February 23rd, the Emperor's Birthday."

"It's January 10th, Dad." Ellie plopped on a vacant bench, lay down in the winter sun and closed her eyes.

"Thank you. I'm well aware of that. The sign says the gardens are open." I pointed across a lawned area which extended for acres into the distance.

"More wandering," said Ellie. She opened her eyes and inspected the park sideways.

"Come on, sleepyhead," said Fiona. "Lean on me. We'll stroll together."

We traversed the park and encountered a monolithic entrance reminiscent of a scene from *Indiana Jones and the Temple of Doom*. High, stone walls framed wooden gates tall enough to permit the entry of a decent-sized Trojan horse, and tiny, human visitors meandered through the gap between them.

"Finally, something's open." I strode forward.

"Here's a map." Fiona tapped a diagram of the gardens. "This section says 'Cherry Trees'." She traced her finger along an image of a gently curving path.

We ambled into the park. High, stone walls weaved among herbaceous borders and reminded me of Mordor. A steep track climbed between them.

"Here we are." I read a sign as we recovered from the ascent. "Cherry tree gardens. Um, the trees look a bit bare."

"Where's the blossoms?" asked Fiona. "I thought one or two might be in early bloom."

Ellie collapsed on the grass. "The fish market's closed, the palace is closed, all the birds have been murdered and the cherry trees are dead. What a great holiday this is."

"Does anyone fancy lunch?" I asked. "Let's see if we can find something authentically Japanese."

Sparse holiday traffic zipped past, and winter sun warmed the top of my head. The road leading away from the palace gardens threaded between conglomerations of skyscrapers; a selection of soaring glass and steel monoliths punctuated by stumpier brown and black structures, like a giant's set of wooden blocks.

All boasted cafés on their ground floors.

Most were closed.

"Can we eat here?" asked Candi, pointing at the first restaurant we'd seen containing diners and staff. "It has free wifi."

I inspected the menu. "This is an American-themed diner, intended for Tokyo residents to experience a taste of the USA. It's not the slightest bit Japanese. I hoped we could eat local food. Remember the rules?"

"Ellie needs a rest." Fiona pointed at our daughter, who reclined in a municipal flower bed and shaded her eyes from the sun. "We'll eat here."

Japanese couples and families crammed the diner, enjoying burgers, ribs and fried chicken. The smell was almost, but not quite, like a TGI Friday's. Something lacked in the aroma emitting from the kitchen, and my nose couldn't decipher exactly which ingredient they'd omitted.

The waitress bowed and indicated with hand symbols we should put on masks. She held up four fingers.

"Yes," I said. "Four people."

American sixties rock 'n' roll music blasted at a volume loud enough to prohibit easy conversation.

Ellie pointed at the menu and shouted. "You wanted something local. Here's a picture of a burger with a Japanese omelette inside it. D'you want fries with that?"

"Bloody hell," I yelled back. "I'm in an oriental version of McDonald's. Okay, I'll have omelette burger with fries. And a beer. A Japanese beer."

She circled her hands around her mouth. "D'you want to add bacon?"

"Yes, please. Bacon improves any meal."

Fiona inspected photographs of the food, bordered by Japanese script. "What are you having?" I mouthed at her.

"Caesar salad."

"You always order Caesar salad. Don't you want something else?"

"I'll pinch some of your chips." She jabbed her finger at my place setting, where she clearly hoped French fries would appear in the near future.

I rolled my eyes. "Why do I never get to eat my whole meal?"

"I'm having fried chicken, chips and salad," said Ellie.

Candi ordered our food by scanning a QR code on the menu and added a beefburger for herself.

A selection of Chuck Berry and Buddy Holly songs played while we waited, and I embarrassed Fiona by singing along loudly enough for diners on adjacent tables to appreciate my entertainment.

"This is almost, but not quite, American diner food," I said, as a server parked an oval plate in front of me. I lifted the top of the burger bun and inspected the contents.

"The chips are authentic." Fiona smiled and reached for the longest one on my plate.

"Could we visit Harajuku now, Dad?" asked Candi, as we recovered from the carbohydrate onslaught, stood on the pavement and perused Google maps.

I narrowed my eyes. "Is that the shopping area?"

"Yes," she said. "It's where all the young, trendy, Japanese teenagers buy their clothes."

Five nursery rhyme door closings later, Kylie led us through the narrow lanes bordered with colourful independent clothes stores. I sniggered to myself and added a further entry to my immature collection of humourous foreign words upon discovering Harajuku's prime shopping boulevard was called Takeshita Street.

I lingered outside hundreds of fitting rooms. Possibly thousands. My three girls entered every one with armfuls of clothes and dumped them on the discard rails as they exited.

"Um, are you going to buy anything?" I asked, as the pile of rejected clothes exceeded those available for purchase in the store. "It's not like we're in Tokyo every day."

"Maybe," said Fiona, idly fondling a pink jumper.

"I might purchase those ripped jeans." Candi pointed at trousers dangling from a hanger which were punctured with so many holes I wondered whether the designer had started with fresh air and worked up from there.

"We could always return tomorrow," said Ellie, depositing a white, fluffy coat on a rack next to five other discarded, white, fluffy coats.

"Tomorrow?" I slapped my forehead. "Tomorrow we're definitely watching sumo. Or singing karaoke. Or eating real sushi. We can't shop every single day."

"Just watch us." Fiona grabbed a jumper and re-entered the fitting room.

"My ticket won't work." I attempted to stuff it into the barrier at Harajuku station. Evening travellers queued behind me.

"This is hopeless." Fiona bared her teeth. "These are 24-hour travelcards."

The regulation friendly, bowing station attendant swung open his cubicle door.

"Excuse me," I said. "Our tickets won't work. We bought them this morning, and they're supposed to last all day."

He bowed and inspected my little square of cardboard.

"This ticket Tokyo Metro."

"Yes. Metro ticket."

"This Yamanote line. Yamanote line not on Tokyo Metro."

"What d'you mean, Yamanote line not on Tokyo Metro? Isn't this Harajuku station?"

"This Harajuku Japan Rail."

"Harajuku Japan Rail is different from Harajuku Metro?"

"Yes. Your ticket for Tokyo Metro. No Japan Rail."

"Is Harajuku Metro station near here?"

He bowed again and pointed into the street. "Harajuku Metro not here. This Harajuku Yamanote line."

"I see. How confusing."

The peace of the ryokan's reception, with the dark-brown furniture, plants and running water, was clearly intended to relax travellers suffering from acute Tokyo train system-stress.

I breathed out and sat heavily on a stool. "All I wanted to do in Japan was eat sushi, sing karaoke and watch sumo wrestling. We haven't achieved any of those today. Instead, we've spent hours on trains, searched for a closed fish market, visited a closed palace, spent ages in clothes shops buying nothing and, in the middle, we ate lunch at a bloody American diner which is supposed to be a foreign experience for the locals. This day's been a complete, utter disaster."

"It's all good," said Fiona. "We still have three whole days in Tokyo. Plenty of time to do what you want to do."

"And more shopping?" asked Candi.

My bottom-bones ground against the floor the following morning as I woke and turned over. "Two nights down, three to go. I'm in bloody agony. The accommodation website didn't say 'bring your own osteopath'."

"I don't know what you're complaining about," said Fiona's voice from the bathroom. "I'm sleeping fine. And I want one of these heated toilet seats at home. I won't be able to live without one in Australia. Could we visit a hardware shop?"

I poked my head around the door. Fiona sat on the loo with a huge smile on her face.

"We are *not* importing a toilet seat," I said. "Heated or otherwise."

Breakfast service commenced with smiling, bowing and production of dolls' tea set-sized cups of coffee.

"I've requested the vegetarian breakfast this morning," I said, draining my coffee in one sip.

"Me too," said Fiona and Ellie simultaneously.

"What did you order, Candi?" I gently pushed her phone away from her eyes.

"Full English."

"Seriously?" My nose wrinkled. "We're in Japan, and you ordered a full English breakfast?"

She nodded violently. "With toast."

The waitress smiled, bowed, placed Candi's tray in front of her and departed to fetch ours.

Fiona inspected the offering. "Those are the smallest sausages and tiniest rashers of bacon I've ever seen. They must breed minuscule pigs here."

"They match the size of the coffee," I said, tipping my thimble of caffeine back in the hope I could discover a final molecule. Could everyone else order coffee too tomorrow, so I can have four? That might almost equal one normal-size drink."

I wolfed my food and pushed my tray away. "Can we book the sumo and the karaoke now? I'm worried we'll leave Japan without seeing them. We wasted a day yesterday."

"Wait until after breakfast, Simon," said Fiona. "Just 'cos you eat like a Labrador doesn't mean we all do."

My fingers tapped on the table until the last mouthfuls of rice, miso soup and toast with a yellowy-brown, unidentifiable spread disappeared.

Fiona scrolled on her phone. "How cool is this? The Grand Sumo Tournament's on while we're here."

"Excellent." I rubbed my hands together.

Fiona's eyebrows raised. "Jeez, tickets are expensive. The cheapest are two hundred dollars for a family."

"It doesn't matter. We can't watch sumo in Australia."

Fiona browsed the website and purchased four tickets for the following day.

"One Tokyo goal sorted," I said. "Could we organise karaoke as well, while you're in an event-booking frame of mind?"

Fiona scrolled and tapped. "There's a karaoke place in a suburb called Shibuya. Would you like to visit this morning at 11:00?"

247

"Sure. We're all singing, right?"

Fiona lifted her eyes from her phone. "I'm not. No-one wants to hear me squawking."

"I've seen Japanese karaoke on YouTube," said Candi. "You sing in a small, private room. Nobody else can hear you."

"You'll be fine," I reached across the table and rubbed Fiona's shoulder. "There's no need to be shy. We'll all clap and cheer for you, whatever you sound like."

She shook her head. "You can sing all you want, Simon. And the girls. I'll take photos." She clicked the 'book' button.

"Two Tokyo goals sorted." I punched the air.

Multiple nursery rhymes and complicated line changes later, we exited the train at Shibuya.

"You know how Dad tells everyone he used to sing in pubs around New Zealand. Now's your chance to hear him." Fiona swung open the door to a bathroom-sized room painted completely black. Luminous stars and moons glowed from the ceiling and, at one end, a wall-mounted, black TV screen for some reason displayed a video of people in swimwear enjoying themselves on a beach. We squeezed around a central table containing an ashtray, two microphones and an iPad.

"How does this machine work?" I asked, twisting the tablet and searching for an 'on' button. "The instructions are in Japanese."

Ellie took it from me, and it lit up. "Which song are you singing, Dad?"

"Um, how about 'Wonderful World'."

She scrolled. "Is it by Sam Cooke?"

"Yes."

"Okay, it's starting."

"What, now? Quick, pass me the microphone."

"Here." Ellie thrust one at me, and I grabbed it in time to begin the third line.

Somehow, I successfully crooned my way through the song, although the lyrics displayed on the screen weren't exactly the same ones Sam Cooke knew and loved.

"Now what?" I asked, as the accompaniment faded, and a copyright notice displayed.

"Our turn," said Candi.

"What d'you want to perform?"

"'Shallow', by Lady Gaga."

The girls followed the highlighted words, then the copyright notice confidently announced they were originally sung by the well-known artist Laddy Gagger.

"Could I have a go?" asked Fiona. She leant forward and peeked at the iPad.

I furrowed my brow. "I thought you didn't want to?"

"Yay, go Mum!" shouted Ellie. "What are you singing?"

Fiona peered at the iPad screen. "Um, 'Hit me Baby One More Time'?"

My eyes opened wide, and I enjoyed a brief, distracting vision of Fiona dressed as Britney Spears. "Really? I imagined you'd choose something more reserved. Maybe a song by The Carpenters?"

Fiona made a vomiting noise. "I hate The Carpenters. Queue it up, Ellie."

The opening riff blared out, and Fiona waited with her head down, and her blonde bob hiding her face.

"We won't be able to hear you," I said. "Hold the microphone to your mouth."

"What, like this?"

Fiona suddenly assumed a rock chick pose, swung her hips provocatively and thrust her pelvis in time to the beat.

"Yes!" I shouted. "Like that." I'd never seen my wife in this guise and grabbed my phone to video her.

"Mum," yelled Candi. "You're embarrassing yourself."

Britney Prior sang the first verse and made suggestive beckoning motions. I showed a tentative thumbs-up as she flicked her hair back and strutted.

The song reached the chorus, and Fiona belted it out at full volume.

KNOCK KNOCK KNOCK

We turned around and stared at the door.

KNOCK KNOCK KNOCK KNOCK

34. SHIBUYA SCRAMBLE

KNOCK KNOCK KNOCK

"Someone's heard you, Mum," said Candi.

KNOCK KNOCK KNOCK

"Open it, Ellie."

"You do it, Dad." Ellie edged away. "I don't know who it is."

I grabbed the doorknob as Fiona reached her vocal climax. Clearly other guests of the establishment had overheard her performance and needed her to sign autographs and pose for selfies. As the final chords of the song crashed and Fiona threw her clenched fist to the ceiling, I opened the door to find a surprised group of four black-suited businessmen.

The corporate group stared at Fiona, statued in her finale pose, her arm in the air, head down and blonde hair covering her face. The music faded, and the screen displayed the copyright notice.

"Ah. Very sorry. Wrong room." They reversed away with much bowing, and I covered a grin with my hand.

"Wow." I hugged her. "We've been married twenty-four years and I never knew you could perform like that."

"Why don't you and Mum sing a duet?" asked Candi, as the music faded.

Fiona and I met eyes.

"Um, any suggestions?" I asked her.

She dragged on an imaginary cigarette. "*Grease?* 'You're the One That I Want?"

"Queue it up, DJ." I plucked the second microphone from the table.

"Oh, my goodness; such fun," said Fiona, outside the karaoke shop. "Could we book another hour tomorrow?"

"We only sang two songs," complained Ellie. "Mum hogged the microphone the whole time."

Fiona grinned. "I want to buy a karaoke machine for home. Is there anywhere to perform in Melbourne? We could book a room for my next birthday?"

I hugged her. "Definitely. But you'll have to wear a Britney outfit." I winked. "What's next on the itinerary?"

Fiona pointed at the street in front of us. "A pedestrian crossing."

"Seriously?" I shook my head. "Even shopping's more exciting. Why the hell would a pedestrian crossing be a tourist attraction?"

"This is Shibuya Scramble Crossing," said Fiona. "The busiest pedestrian crossing in the world."

"It's always on Instagram, Dad," said Candi. She scrolled, typed and thrust her phone at me. "It even has free wifi."

A throng of Japanese office workers stood at the corners of the star-shaped unintentional tourist attraction, which resembled a herd of cartoon zebras flattened by a passing steamroller. The winter sun warmed our faces as we poised, ready to join the Insta-crowds. Immediately the tweety-birds sounded, a mass traversing swarmed from every direction over the steamrollered zebras. I slipped my phone from my pocket and snapped two photos of us in mid-Israelite pose before the waters of the Red Sea engulfed us.

The crowd thinned, and the lights changed in favour of the traffic.

"Now what?" I said.

Fiona grinned and swivelled around. "Now we cross back again."

I blew a raspberry. "No wonder this is the busiest crossing in the world if everyone's taking pictures of themselves crossing it."

We waited for the tweety birds and dodged fellow zebra-crossers to return to the spot we'd started from.

"Now," directed Fiona, as if she were Roman Polanski, "Candi and Ellie, could you cross by yourselves, and I'll take a photo of you when you return?"

"Okay, Mum," said Candi. "Don't post it anywhere without my permission."

The electronic birds tweeted; the girls crossed, they waited obediently with ten thousand Israelites on the other side, then marched back for Fiona's photo.

"I think," I said, "we may have exhausted the excitement of this activity."

"Can we buy lunch at a cat café now?" Ellie grinned and hugged herself. "I want to play with the kitties."

"Food and cute animals," said Candi. "Does it get any better?" She scrolled her phone and gasped. "Hey, Ellie. Five minutes' walk away, there's a hedgehog café."

"Hedgehog café?" I glanced at Fiona, and we both raised our eyebrows.

"Yep," said Candi. "We can pat hedgehogs. Here come some great photos."

"Hedgehog café. 2F," said Fiona, as we waited for a tiny lift.

"That means it's on the second floor," I said. "I've worked that out. And there's no floor called 'ground' in Japan, so we go up one level."

The hedgehog café lady bowed and smiled behind her mask. As I'd expected, she spoke no English, so she brandished a laminated card with colourful pictures resembling Beatrix Potter's *Mrs Tiggywinkle*.

Ellie glanced around the room which was bordered by a wall-mounted chest-high bench where children and adults oohed and aahed over tiny, spiky animals. "Dad, Dad, look. They have their own dolls' houses." She lay a hand over her heart. "Oh, my goodness, they're so cute."

"You can buy the hedgehogs," said Candi, reading a sign. "Could we take one home?"

"I don't think we'd be allowed to import a live animal," said Fiona.

Ellie fluttered her eyelashes at me. "Dad, I need to pat a hedgehog."

Despite the cost, I couldn't refuse my daughters this unique experience.

"All right. We'll book you two in. Mum and I'll find a snack while you play."

"Thanks, Dad." Ellie stared around the room and sighed happily.

"Hedgehog café," I said, as Fiona and I stepped out of the lift on the ground floor. "Whatever next?"

"I don't think I'd fancy playing with them. Too spiky. I still want to visit a cat café, though." She took my hand. "For our lunch, how about Wendy Burger next door? Remember how we used to enjoy them in London?"

"I'm beginning to wonder if we'll finish our Tokyo holiday without eating at a Japanese restaurant."

Two Wendy burgers later, we returned to the hedgehog café to find Candi with a brown-and-white mouse crawling through her hair.

"Dad, can we buy him?"

"No way," said Fiona. "There's no chance I'm having a mouse in my home. Eeeurggh."

"But he's so cute," said Candi, as the mouse ran from her left to right hand and forced her to discard her phone. "I've had so many comments on my feed about him."

I glanced over Ellie's shoulder and furrowed my brow. "What d'you have there? A pale, long-nosed hedgehog?"

She thrust her hand at me which contained a small, inquisitive, spiky creature. "It's a tenrec. A species of mammal within the afrotherian family, endemic to Madagascar. They're wildly diverse owing to convergent evolution."

"Oh. Erm, cute." The wildly diverse tenrec sat on her shoulder and whiffled its nose. "Have you played with the hedgehogs?"

"We've played with everything. The café wants us to buy one. The lady keeps pointing at the animals and showing us prices."

"Right. Obviously, we can't purchase anything. It's time to leave. Put the animals back in the, err, dolls houses."

"Bye, bye, Tenrec," said Ellie. She placed the tiny animal into a vacant bedroom where it stood and sniffed at her.

"I want to keep the mouse," said Candi. "D'you think they'll notice if I put it in my pocket?"

"I'll notice." Fiona stepped back. "Get rid of it. Horrible thing. Let's go shopping."

My eyes widened. "More shopping?"

"Yep. Back to Takeashita street. We can walk from here."

I found myself again waiting outside hundreds of changing rooms. Fiona discovered a store for petite Japanese ladies which sold underwear in her size, and every couple of minutes, her arm reached around the changing room curtain and threw a bra at me, with the instruction to find a different size, or a different colour, or a different material. I didn't usually object to Fiona removing her bra and throwing it at me, but I was happy to make an exception on this occasion.

Multiple trains, bowings and nursery rhymes later, we arrived back at the ryokan and entered our rooms.

"I'm going straight to sleep," Fiona spluttered through a mouthful of toothpaste. She extracted the complimentary toothbrush from her lips and cleaned it. "We've a big day tomorrow. Sumo first, then the Toyosu fish market. We'll be able to buy sushi made from fish fresh off the boat."

"Real sushi? Made by a real sushi chef?"

"Yep."

"Excellent." I fist-pumped. "My final Japan goal ticked off."

"And," said Fiona, tugging on her pyjamas, "We must find a cat café. Hedgehogs and mice aren't exactly my thing."

I lay down on my bed and winced as my spine touched the floorboards.

We must have settled into the vegetarian rice, egg and miso soup breakfast, as everyone ordered it that morning. Japanese hospitality didn't extend to teaspoons, so I idly stirred my coffee with the wrong end of a chopstick, swallowed the contents of the miniature cup in one gulp and inspected the sumo tickets, which stated they remained valid for the entire day.

"Let's go to sumo after breakfast," I said. "I've heard the more famous wrestlers appear in the afternoon, and the arena becomes busy. We don't care if we see famous or not-so-famous ones, right? We want to watch the experience."

Fiona nodded. "Okay, and after that, lunch at Toyosu fish market. I checked, and it's definitely open today."

"We won't have to ask at the Tsukiji station so-called Information Centre?"

"Nope. I know exactly where I'm going. Candi, could you find us a cat café?"

Candi took twenty pictures of her breakfast, then swiped her phone and frowned. "Which suburb's the sumo in?"

"It says Ryōgoku on the tickets," I said.

She scrolled.

"And where's the fish market?"

"Toyosu. Why?"

She swiped rapidly. "There's no cat cafés near either."

"Okay. We'll need to visit another suburb."

She paused mid-swipe and opened her eyes wide. "Woah, Dad. You'll want to see this."

"What?" I leant towards her.

Candi pointed to her device. "Do we go anywhere near Kichijōji?"

"Kichijōji? I haven't heard of it. What's there?"

"This." She shoved her screen in my face. "Your dream."

I leant back. "Where's my glasses? What am I looking at?"

"It's a cat café."

"So?"

"They also have another animal there."

"More hedgehogs?"

"No. Can't you see it?" She removed her phone from my face and increased the image size with two forefingers.

"What? Don't keep me in suspense."

"Look."

"I am looking."

"Oh, for goodness' sake. The photo. What is it?"

I blew the picture up further, stared, and my hand flew to my mouth. "Bloody hell. Is that real?" My eyes opened as wide as dustbin lids. "Is that what I think it is?"

Candi withdrew the phone. "Yep. You can thank me later."

"What is it?" asked Fiona.

I grabbed Candi's phone and shoved it in her face. "Look! The cat café in this suburb called Kichijōji. Look what it has. Look."

I paused and exhaled.

"This cat café also owns a capybara."

35. FURIGANA

Fiona recoiled from the experience of the screen being stuffed in her nose. "I don't believe you."

"See?" I poked the phone's screen. "There are pictures of people patting cats and stroking capybaras. Wait there. I'll fetch my laptop to see a bigger photo."

I ran to the lift, jabbed at the button and wondered why elevators were invariably on another floor when you were in a hurry.

Four minutes later, I plopped back at the breakfast table and flung open the laptop's lid.

"What's the web address, Candi?"

"Capy Neko Café."

"Capyneko.cafe? Is this the right website? Oh. My. Goodness. Foster parent recruitment-type café." I turned to Candi. "D'you reckon they'd let us adopt a capybara? We could keep it in the garden. I could grow lettuces for it to eat, and maybe it'd keep the lawn down?"

"Mum wouldn't let me have a teeny-weeny little mouse yesterday, so you've no chance with a capybara."

"Too right," said Fiona. "You're not bringing a giant rodent home. I'm not sure I even want to see it."

An album of website photographs displayed grinning Japanese people stroking a contented capybara.

"Bloody hell. This place had better be open." I swept my arm and knocked over one of the tiny teacups. "Where is this Kichijōji suburb? Fiona, d'you have the train map?"

Fiona unfolded the A4-sized diagram of Japan's multiple train networks, all helpfully presented on the same page as if they interconnected sensibly, which was a complete fallacy.

"Kichijōji has to be in Tokyo." I scrolled through websites frantically. "If it's in Osaka or another city we'll be riding the bullet train."

"Or not seeing this particular capybara?" suggested Fiona.

"What d'you mean, not seeing it?" My hands flapped wildly, and Ellie relocated other pieces of china before I broke anything. "I missed out in England; I have to see this one. There's no option."

Fiona rolled her eyes.

"Here it is. Yes!" I hugged her, and she pulled away. "Kichijōji's in Tokyo. But the suburb's not on the metro." I flicked my laptop's touch screen. "It's beyond the boundaries of the city map. We take a train to the end of the Marunouchi line, alight at a station called Ogikubo, then take a different service called the Chuo line two stops to Kichijōji."

"That sounds complicated," said Fiona. "How long will it take?"

"Google maps says ninety minutes from the centre. Let's book for late afternoon, after we've been to the fish market."

"And the sumo," said Ellie.

I found the booking page. "The only availability's 5.30pm. Let's go then. In case we have more problems with the trains, and it takes us hours to reach Kichijōji."

"Are you sure this'll be worth it?" asked Fiona.

"Are you crazy?" My eyes goggled at her. "Of course it'll be worth it. I've been wanting to meet a capybara all my life."

"Not all your life, Dad," said Ellie. "You didn't know about them when you were born."

"All right, clever clogs. Since my teenage years."

I clicked the 5:30 button, and the website opened another screen completely in Japanese.

"Help! Now what do I do?"

Candi peered over my shoulder. "Click the Union Jack. There. Now it's in English."

Fiona grabbed my arm. "Slow down. Stop panicking. I'm sure they won't sell out."

"Look at this." I read the screen. "Customers can take pictures with the capybara, relax on the sofa and interact with it as if they were at home." I grinned. "This'll be the best day of my life."

Fiona tilted her head. "Better than our wedding day?"

I smiled. "Okay, the second-best day of my life."

Ellie glared. "Better than the day we were born?"

"For goodness' sake. The third best. It'll be the third-best day of my life."

I typed '4' in the number-of-people box and clicked 'reserve'. Entering my surname and first name presented no problems, but I paused on the third box and glanced upwards.

"What's Furigana double-byte Katakana?"

"No idea," said Fiona. "Why?"

"It's asking me for my name in"—I traced my fingers along the sentence—"Furigana (Sei) and Furigana (May) double-byte Katakana. It won't let me progress without completing those boxes."

"Why don't you try entering your name in English again?" asked Ellie.

I typed 'Prior' and 'Simon' into the boxes and pressed 'proceed to confirmation'. A bright-red circle appeared.

"It doesn't understand my name." I slumped in my chair. "What are we going to do? I must see the capybara. I can't miss out because of this stupid website."

"Maybe we could turn up at 5:30 without a booking?" suggested Fiona.

"No. It says maximum ten people per time slot. We can't risk it."

Candi showed me her phone. "I found an English to Katakana translator."

"Seriously? Furigana double-byte Katakana?"

"I suppose so. Visit the website and try for yourself."

I navigated to the web address Candi gave me and entered "Simon."

The box underneath returned: **サイモン**

I puffed out my cheeks, then gave her a thumbs-up. "This works."

My hands trembled as I pasted the Furigana double-byte Katakana into the capybara booking form and typed 'Prior' into the translator.

The translator displayed: **プライアー**

I pasted my newly acquired Japanese surname, completed my email address and phone number and pressed 'proceed to confirmation'.

The website paused.

I watched the spinning circle of doubt.

And waited.

"Fingers crossed, everyone." I crossed every crossable appendage.

Pause.

"Come on, come on. This has to work."

Spinning circle.

"Please…"

A pop-up appeared in Japanese. I had no idea what the characters meant, but the big green tick inside a circle required no translation.

"Yes!" I pulled Fiona out of her seat and waltzed her around the room. "A booking for the best day of my life."

"I'm glad we bought these 24-hour travelcards last night," I said, as we changed trains at Naka-okachimachi station on our way to see the sumo wrestling. Crowds of people dashed around us; headphones on, faces in phones. No conversation.

"We can use them again today," said Fiona, "and if we return from the capybara place before 8:00 pm we won't have to buy more tickets. Some of these line changes are ridiculous, though. The one yesterday, where we had to surface, walk five hundred metres along the street and enter another station wasn't a proper connection."

After a long walk down a tunnel, we arrived at Naka-okachimachi's sister station: Ueno-okachimachi.

I pointed at an overhead sign. "We need the Oedo line for the sumo. Ryōgoku's at E12, and we're at E9. Twelve minus nine is three, so it's three stops."

"Are you finally getting this metro system sorted out, Dad?" asked Ellie.

"I reckon so. It's easy once you understand it."

Candi inserted her square of cardboard, and the machine immediately spat it back at her.

She turned it over in her hand. "The machine won't accept my ticket, Dad."

"Let me try," I pushed my ticket in, with an identical rejection. "Weird. These last twenty-four hours, and we bought them yesterday evening."

"Ask the ticket dude," said Ellie, as a friendly bowing station attendant appeared from his cubicle.

I bowed to him. "Excuse me. Our tickets won't work. We bought them last night, and they're supposed to be 24-hour travelcards."

He bowed and inspected my ticket with two hands.

"This ticket Tokyo Metro."

"Yes. Metro ticket."

"Oedo line not Tokyo Metro."

"What d'you mean, Oedo line not Tokyo Metro?" I ran a hand through my hair. "It's on the same map."

"Oedo line not Tokyo Metro. Oedo line Tokyo Subway."

"Tokyo Metro is different from Tokyo Subway?"

The station attendant bowed and pointed with his white-gloved hand.

"Your ticket Tokyo Metro. No Tokyo Subway. Very sorry. You buy Tokyo Subway ticket." He indicated the ticket machine, and I sighed and wiggled my hand into my cash pocket.

Two security guards stopped us at the Kokugikan Sumo Stadium entrance, inspected us, inspected our bags, inspected our tickets, bowed multiple times and waved us inside. We stepped into a large, high-ceilinged hall. Flights of stairs led to the left and right, and colourful advertisements displayed action shots of sumo wrestling under bright writing detailing dates and times.

"Are we here on the correct day?" I asked. "It seems empty."

"They have free wifi," announced Candi, as she buried herself in Snapchat.

"I'm tired," said Ellie. "Can we sit down?"

A young lady dressed in a black skirt and smart jacket guarded one of the entrances to the central arena.

"Excuse me," said Fiona. She showed her the tickets. "Where are these seats?"

I tiptoed to glance behind the staff member. "I hope they're in this section. This has an amazing view, close to the stage."

The lady beckoned and began to march along the walkway encircling the stadium. We followed her, passing multiple double doors sentried by similarly uniformed people. At each one, I caught a distant glimpse into the arena, where kimono-clad staff members prepared a raised dais which resembled a stumpy, red, Mayan pyramid. The guide turned and led us up a flight of stairs.

And another flight of stairs.

And another flight of stairs.

The view became more distant, but I still clearly saw the wrestlers. Our usher circumnavigated the next level of the arena, and we followed obediently. At one point she paused and re-inspected our tickets. After a left wheel, she set off up a further flight of stairs.

And another flight of stairs.

And another flight of stairs into the arena's top tier, where empty seats surrounded us.

We ascended an aisle to the point where I wondered if we'd need oxygen tanks to deal with the altitude.

At the top row of the top tier, she held one arm straight out and bowed.

We'd summited and glimpsed the sumo stage at base camp several kilometres below us.

"Why are we all the way up here?" I hissed at Fiona as we shuffled into our seats.

"Because we booked the cheapest tickets."

"Yes, but all the seats are empty. D'you think we could move down a bit?" I slid into a row three below ours.

"Dad," said Candi. "You can't sit in someone else's seat."

"Why not? Nobody's looking."

"Because it's not what you do in Japan. Come back up here and watch."

"Okay. Did you bring a telescope?"

I leant forward and clasped my hands as four older men robed in black processed into the arena like vicars at a Church of England funeral. Each sat cross-legged on a square, red mat, one on each side of the podium's base. I presumed they were officials or judges and strained my eyes to see distant details.

The quiet steps of the bare-footed participants echoed around the empty stadium as they followed.

A man wearing a bright-green kimono stepped into the centre of the dais, bowed and addressed the sparse, widely dispersed crowd by singing a lengthy, operatic song. He brandished a fan in a symbolic action.

Once he'd completed his Japanese Toreador, he bowed some more, lifted a broom of the style used by the witch in *Hansel and Gretel* and swept grains of sand from the podium's perimeter.

Concurrent with the sweeping ritual, a white kimono-robed man stepped up and bowed. Two impressively sturdy wrestlers followed him and faced the audience from opposite edges of the dais. They stretched, flexed their arms and legs, stamped, bowed and generally demonstrated their potential for extinguishing the average man merely by sitting on him. I noted one Michelin man-contestant possessed significantly greater girth than the other and made a mental note to analyse how often the thinner man won, as I understood sumo to be as much about skill and mental preparation as physical size.

An announcer's voice intonated a lengthy biography of the two wrestlers. The white-kimonoed man, whom I took to be the referee, stood on one leg in a statue-like pose.

He motioned with his fan.

Everybody bowed to each other a lot.

He spoke a short, sharp command.

The competitors crouched and faced each other, as the referee flexed his fan backward with a minute wrist movement.

This was the signal everyone had anticipated.

36. BONZAI

The wrestlers grabbed each other, clasped bodies briefly, then one pushed the other out of the ring in a bout lasting two seconds.

They faced off again, bowed and stepped from the dais. One member of the sparse audience clapped loudly.

"Is that it?" Candi frowned.

"It's all about the ritual," I said. "The wrestling is a small part of it."

Ellie puffed. "I can't believe we paid fifty dollars each to watch a two-second fight."

"Ssh." I jammed a finger to my lips, as the green kimono-clad singer returned for a second aria, and the spectacle repeated with two new contestants.

The operatic solo.

Sand sweeping.

Wrestlers bowing, stamping and flexing their limbs.

Biographical announcements.

Discreet, minute fan-motions from the referee.

Two seconds of body grappling, and a final, polite bow.

I loved it. The procedure, the spectacle, the tradition. I stared and watched the performance play out again and again. Private bets with myself as to which wrestler would win confirmed the larger contestant almost always triumphed.

Ellie leant on Fiona's shoulders and closed her eyes.

Candi scrolled her phone.

After two hours of succinct, similar bouts, unexpected excitement occurred when one of the larger wrestlers pushed his opponent off the dais on top of a judge.

Fiona tapped me on the shoulder. "I think I've seen enough. Shall we go to the fish market now?"

We descended the multiple levels of the sumo stadium and rested at ground level.

"Where is this fish market?" I asked, pointing at my watch. "Do we have time to visit it? I've already missed out on one encounter with a capybara this holiday; I'm not missing another."

Ellie clenched her teeth. "Dad, we have over five hours until our appointment at the capybara café."

"I know, but we don't know how long it'll take to get there, or exactly where it is. We might get lost."

"Yes, and we might not. What about your sushi holiday goal?"

"Meeting the capybara's a life goal. It trumps a holiday goal."

"Calm down, we can fit both in," said Fiona. "And maybe some shopping."

"No way do we have time for more shopping," I spluttered. "If we're late for the capybara because of bloody shopping, I'll…"

Fiona winked. "Shopping *after* the capybara."

The train doors slid open at Toyosu station to the accompaniment of 'Baa Baa Black Sheep.'

"Okay, Google," I addressed the phone. "Toyosu Fish Market."

"You have arrived," said Kylie, doubtfully.

"No, we haven't." I enjoyed disagreeing with Kylie, the one woman I could contradict without repercussions.

I swivelled on my heels and searched among the buildings for anything resembling a fish market.

"The market will be at the docks, won't it?" asked Fiona. "Tell Kylie to direct us there."

"Okay, Google. Tokyo docks."

Kylie led us on a circumnavigation of the station, and we strode through a modern, industrial area. Bright, shiny, monolithic exteriors unblemished by weather-stains framed both sides of the road and seemed to have been constructed in the last few weeks. In the unlikely event an Everest double-glazing salesman chanced upon this street, his commission wouldn't have covered his bar tab. I didn't notice a single window.

Nothing resembled a fish market.

Fiona stopped a man swinging a briefcase. "Excuse me? Fish market?"

He bowed and frowned simultaneously. "Fish market?"

"Yes. Toyosu Fish Market?"

"Ah. Toyosu." He grinned, pointed back the way we'd come, bowed again and continued walking.

"He thought you meant Toyosu station," said Candi. "Not the fish market."

We marched a further kilometre past faceless, giant-size shoeboxes, then waited while a man wearing a hi-viz vest supervised roadworks at a pedestrian crossing.

"Excuse me," said Fiona. "Fish market?"

He bowed and pointed up a metal staircase which punctured the second floor of one of the shoeboxes.

"I can see the entrance," said Fiona. "The sign says, 'Fish Market'. We're here."

At the top of the metal staircase, an elevated walkway terminated in a sandwich board. 'Fish market. Open 5:00am to 1:00pm.'

"I can't believe it." Fiona looked at her watch and slumped. "We're too late."

We stared at the sandwich board as if this action would alter its message.

"Since we're here," she said, "we may as well enter. Maybe there's something to see."

Inside, we discovered a row of twelve small restaurants, advertising assorted forms of fish and seafood.

Chinese.

Thai.

Korean.

Tepanyaki.

Almost-British-style cod and chips.

I tipped my head back and inhaled the fusion of flavours.

"Here," I said, and ducked into a tiny establishment, empty save for three bored-looking sushi chefs and a waitress. She seated us at a tiny table and dropped four laminated menus, the combined acreage of which exceeded the size of the tabletop.

"Let's buy two dishes and share them," said Fiona, casting her eyes down the list of food. "This place is expensive."

"Authentic, fresh sushi won't be cheap." I studied the menu from top to bottom.

The waitress clinked a thimble of water in front of each of us.

Fiona pointed. "Could we order two dishes to share?" She made a circle motion above the table with her finger to illustrate her request.

The server bowed. "Sorry. One food, one person."

"I see," said Fiona. She indicated entrées at the top of the menu. "Four of these, please."

The server bowed again. "Sorry. These not for lunch."

"Far out," said Fiona. "It's very difficult to order anything."

I grabbed the card and jabbed a picture in the middle. "Is everyone okay with this one?"

"Yes," said Candi. "Anything. I'm starving."

"I'm happy with whatever," said Ellie.

"It's almost one hundred dollars," said Fiona.

"Four of these," I said to the server, as I pressed my forefinger against the picture.

She bowed and reversed away.

"When will we have the chance again to eat sushi fresh from the boat, prepared by a properly qualified chef in his native country?" I whispered to Fiona. "So what if it's one hundred dollars? We're paying for the experience."

Ten minutes later, a sushi chef slid four wooden boards over the divider between the food preparation area and our table.

I sampled a piece, paused and chewed slowly. "I've never had sushi this fresh. The fish must've been caught this morning." I turned the food over in my mouth and willed it to last longer and not melt on my tongue. "This is nothing like the dried-up rubbish in food courts at home."

"Yay, there's no plastic packaging," said Ellie. "And the boards and chopsticks are reusable."

"It's yummy," said Candi. "I could eat that all over again."

"Have you finished already? This isn't fish and chips from the corner shop. You're supposed to savour it."

"Sorry. I was hungry."

After lunch, we discovered a room where we could view a video showing what the fish market would've looked like if it was open, which we probably could've seen on YouTube.

I hurried my family away as soon as the video finished. "Come on." I tugged Fiona's arm. "We only have three-and-a-half hours until the capybara café appointment."

"Exactly," said Ellie. "We'll be hours early."

"We don't know where it is." I marched ahead and called over my shoulder. "We have to cross the whole of Tokyo, using goodness knows how many train lines, none of which will match up properly, with tickets which won't be interchangeable for any of them, then once we exit the train at the other end, I'm not sure exactly where the café is." I threw my hands in the air. "And the suburb's beyond the end of the metro. Once we reach Ogikubo station we take some other kind of overground train a couple of stops. I'm sure that'll need an additional ticket and more money. We can't be late."

Twenty minutes' quick march later, we arrived back at Toyosu station, and I inspected the train map.

"This is ridiculous," I said. "Not only are the lines not all integrated, but they're not shown on the same map. Now which train do we take?"

Fiona traced over the map with her finger. "The brown line to Nagatacho, then the red line to Ogikubo. That's the postbox-red line. Not the rose-red line or the magenta-red line. I hope Japanese people have good eyesight; they'd be in trouble if they couldn't distinguish colours clearly."

"The lines have letters," said Ellie. "All the letters are different. We're travelling on the Y line, then the M line."

"I understand that bit. But why is the Yurikamome line the U line? It doesn't have a U in it."

"Because Y was already taken by the Yurakucho line. The one we're going on."

"I thought I'd worked this out." I shook my head. "We'd better hurry, in case we become lost."

After multiple nursery rhymes on the Y line, a complicated time-consuming change at Nagatacho station and further nursery rhymes on the M line, we arrived at the last station on the metro, way out in the distant Tokyo suburbs. Our expedition banged up against the left-hand edge of the map, and we now ventured into unexplored lands.

"One more train," I said. "We take the Chou main line two stops to Kichijōji station, then work out where the capybara café is from there."

"This capybara better be worth it," said Fiona, shaking her head slowly. "I'm sick of all these trains."

"How can you say that?" I threw both hands in the air. "Of course it'll be worth it."

I inspected the ticket machine. "We might not be travelling on another train, anyway. This machine only takes cash, and I spent the last of ours on sushi."

"How far is it to walk?" asked Ellie.

"Walk? Don't be silly. Miles."

"How can it be miles if it's two stops on the train?"

"These are main line trains. Not underground trains. It could be a long distance between stations."

Candi waved her phone. "Google maps says it's forty-five minutes."

270

"How d'you have connectivity? Have you found free wifi?"

"I'm tethered to something called Takumi's iPhone 14." She gazed around. "He might be cute."

I laughed. "He might be an old man."

"He owns an iPhone 14. He's not an old man."

"I can manage forty-five minutes' walk," said Ellie. We have almost two hours until the capybara appointment. Let's explore suburban Tokyo, see how people live and work, suck in more culture."

"Okay," I said. "We'll walk the forty-five minutes. Hopefully we see an ATM, so I can withdraw cash for the return journey."

"And we need to buy fruit," said Fiona. "My body's crying out for fresh food."

"Mine, too," said Ellie. "I'm sick of this packaged, convenience store rubbish."

"Right. ATM, fruit and capybaras. Everybody ready? Okay, Google. Take me to capybara heaven."

"Now playing 'Take me to Heaven' on Spotify," announced Kylie, joyfully.

"Gah. Why does she have to be so literal?"

After receiving instructions which she could understand, Kylie chaperoned us along a narrow, dark passageway which I was glad I didn't have to negotiate alone after nightfall. We traipsed past a deserted Buddhist temple, then our route traversed a bridge and followed a long, straight street framed with small, independent shops.

All of them sold products which seemed to have incredibly specific niche markets.

Tools used for exercising wrists.

Tiny knives with blades one inch long.

Salt shakers of every size and material.

"I don't hold out hope of finding a bank here," I said, as Fiona and Ellie inspected a window displaying dusty, ornate Bonzai tools.

"Nor a fruit shop," said Fiona.

"And there's no wifi in this suburb," said Candi, as she rotated on one heel with her phone in the air like a pirouetting Statue of Liberty.

"There's a post office." I pointed. "They'll have an ATM."

At this point, my bucket list capybara goal was about to be impacted independently by three elderly people, all of whom would detain us, and all of whom would give us individual insights into the wonderful politeness and consideration of Japanese manners.

Three post office tellers dealt with customers, separated from them by glass partitions. I smiled as the usual transactions took place as they would have done in England, or Australia, and cash and documents passed between the public and the staff.

A fourth employee stood next to an ATM, alongside an extremely tiny elderly lady. Although I couldn't understand the conversation, it was clear the lady had no idea how the ATM functioned, nor potentially what its purpose was, but the staff member delivered an intense training course with much bowing and extraordinary patience.

I took a deep breath.

The employee stopped short of pressing the controls for the old lady, which would've helped, as she was too short to read the writing on each button. Instead, the staff member helpfully pointed, and the lady pushed each knob with a short, stumpy finger. At one point, it seemed she'd made a fatal mistake, and with much apologising and bowing, the post office worker retrieved her bank card and recommenced the entire process.

If this scene had played out in any western country, the staff member would become politely exasperated, the customer would feel stupid and I'd tap my foot behind them and mutter loudly, "Goodness, is it four o'clock already? How time flies."

None of this occurred.

The employee carefully extricated the old lady's card and helped her re-insert it into the slot, which was approximately the same height as her forehead, then began the button pressing demonstration again.

Characters on the screen flashed, the staff member tugged notes from the drawer, bowed and presented the old lady with her money reverentially in two hands.

The customer then spent several minutes battling with the clasp of her handbag until it clicked open and enveloped the cash.

The post office employee smiled and bowed.

The old lady smiled and bowed.

I smiled and bowed, although I wasn't sure whether I should, as I hadn't been an active participant in the transaction.

Once I discovered the 'English' button, I achieved my withdrawal without the help of a smiling, bowing assistant, and grasped five one-thousand-yen notes.

Let's take a minute to think about this.

I'm transiting through a distant, unimportant suburb of Tokyo, which until our decision to walk to the capybara café, I've no idea I'll visit. I haven't advised anyone at my bank I'm leaving Australia, let alone visiting Japan. Yet here, in this tiny, suburban post office, where tellers still offer step-by-step assistance to elderly residents, I'm able to insert a piece of plastic I've brought with me into a machine and receive, from my own bank account, significant amounts of cash.

Instantly.

I still find the concept of this technology mind-boggling.

"We have cash now." I slipped the notes into an inner pocket. "We have the means to travel back again. Let's walk faster to make up time."

"And," said Fiona, "we can buy fruit."

"After the capybara?"

"We have ages, Dad," said Ellie. "If we see a fruit shop, we're stopping."

We marched down the street's endless, dead-straight path. Ubiquitous junk shops continued to populate both sides; their doors shuttered, and their lights extinguished. With the exception of the Post Office, we hadn't seen a single store which looked like any customers had populated it in decades. Possibly ever.

Ellie and Fiona paused at a glass-fronted establishment. Small, wooden crates contained fruit and vegetables.

"At last." Ellie blew out like a horse. "A shop selling something useful."

Fiona weighed a cabbage in her cupped hands. "I'm dying for anything green. Let's buy one of these."

"How are we going to cook it?" I asked. "We don't have a stove. Or a microwave."

"Oh, yes. These apples look good. Three hundred yen each."

I looked at my watch. "Could you choose one quicker, please?"

"Shall we buy four?" asked Fiona. She began to select fresh, crisp fruit.

"Wait, Mum," said Ellie. "This box contains apples for one hundred yen each. They have spots on them, but it won't matter. It's good to buy imperfect fruit." She chose four apples with assorted blemishes, and we entered the shop to pay.

I had the immediate impression nobody visited this store on a regular basis. Certainly not today. Displays of deli meats and various tins and packets with unfamiliar logos stood back-to-back against chest fridges one-quarter-filled with packets of assorted fish.

"Hello?" I called into the empty shop. "Konnichiwa?"

A cough sounded in a rear room, and a lady who could've been a twin of my ATM-challenged friend shuffled out. She held onto a display to steady herself and greeted us with a minute bow from the neck. I ruminated on how we might've been the first non-Japanese customers she'd ever hosted.

Ellie dumped the four imperfect apples on the counter, and I placed a five hundred yen note next to them.

The lady looked up at me as if I were a complete lunatic.

37. KI-CHAN

The elderly lady threatened me with the first apple and carefully tapped on each blemish with her blotchy, clawed hands.

Individually.

Slowly.

"It's okay," said Fiona. "We don't mind the spots."

"I'm sure she doesn't speak English," whispered Candi.

The shopkeeper shook her head and rotated each apple individually in front of Fiona, pointing out each accusatory mark.

Was this gaijin (foreigner) insane? Did she not realise the fruit she planned to buy was *substandard*?

I huffed and checked my watch. In fifty-five minutes, my allotted timeslot featured in the capybara's calendar; Google maps stated we had twenty-five minutes' walk, and we still weren't sure of the exact address.

The elderly lady paused after the fourth apple and jabbed a stumpy, bent finger towards the tray of perfect, three-hundred-yen fruit. She challenged Ellie to swap them.

Ellie pushed the spotty apples over the counter with the five hundred yen note. "We're happy with these. Arigatō (Thank you)."

Resigned to the fact these stupid foreigners were determined to buy fruit clearly unfit for human consumption, the lady stabbed buttons on the till and accepted the money.

We bowed, stuffed the apples in our pockets and escaped from the shop.

"That was exhausting," said Fiona. "How does she ever sell anything?"

"Come on." I strode ahead, turned around and addressed my family while walking backward. "We can't be late. How did two hours early turn into just-in-time?"

"Turn right," requested Kylie, and the map on my phone proceeded to describe a complicated zigzag through cramped, narrow, residential streets. We passed ordinary Japanese people's daily lives played out before us.

A lady reversing a tiny car into a space millimetres bigger than it, performing a manoeuvre she'd clearly executed many times. I wondered how she'd cope if the family ever purchased a larger vehicle.

Three small children frolicking on the asphalt, watched by a parent from an upstairs window. They had no option but to play in the street, their houses didn't boast a square metre of outdoor space.

Verdant foliage sprouting vertically in a passageway barely wide enough to walk through sideways. This was the resident's garden. Half a metre square by three metres high.

Everything squashed in, and in a Lilliputian way, perfectly formed.

We came to the end of the residential streets and burst out onto a main road.

"Turn right," repeated Kylie, confidently.

"One kilometre to go." I marched towards a distant commercial area. Kylie directed us across the highway via a pedestrian bridge into another residential area on the opposite side, a mirror of the one with the kids and vertical gardens. We strode into ever-decreasing thoroughfares.

"You have arrived," announced Kylie, a little uncertainly.

I stopped, frowned at the phone, held it up and swivelled.

Rows of two-storey houses cramped up against each other, behind tiny parking spaces, some of which embraced micro-cars.

A lady carrying shopping bags entered a house. She ducked her head and avoided meeting our eyes.

No other humans populated the streets.

"There are no cafés here. This can't be right. We've come to the wrong place." I slumped. "It's almost five o'clock. Now we'll be late for the appointment, and I'll never meet the capybara."

"Are you sure this isn't correct? Maybe it's situated in someone's house?" suggested Fiona. "Maybe the capybara's their pet and we see it in their front room?"

"No. I know it's in a café from the website photos. Let's return to the main road. It must be around here somewhere."

We doubled back down a side street and came across a school.

In every country I've travelled to: England, the United States, Australia, New Zealand, everywhere, outside a primary school in the late afternoon a school crossing supervisor maintains duty. They emerge from the same internationally available mould. A lady or man of early retirement age, immaculately turned out in a municipally supplied, luminous orange or yellow coat, wielding the two symbols of their responsibility and power; artefacts equivalent to the King of England's orb and sceptre.

1. The Whistle of Obedience. Until the unique blast of this instrument pierces the air, every school child is aware they must wait safely on the pavement.

2. The Pole of Threat. Brandished like a religious ensign, with the prominent letters: STOP: CHILDREN, on sight of this, every car driver knows they must halt their vehicle directly.

I couldn't decipher the Japanese calligraphy on this man's stick, but the significance was clear. His young charges had departed, and he idly waited for the end of his shift. I figured the chances of him understanding or speaking enough English to help me were minimal, but I had no-one else to ask.

He bowed.

I bowed.

"Konbanwa," I said.

This was a good start. He smiled behind his mask, bowed again and clearly anticipated further discourse in his native tongue.

"Could you tell me the way to Café Neko?"

Pause.

His brow furrowed so deeply it resembled a freshly ploughed field.

My optimism of communication evaporated gradually as we waited before him. My lifelong dream, my bucket list goal hung on the linguistic abilities of a school crossing supervisor in an insignificant Tokyo suburb.

Pause.

"Café Neko. Aah." He placed a thumb and forefinger on his head and closed his eyes.

Cogs in his brain revolved, as he dredged English words from his long-term memory he possibly hadn't used since his own primary school education sixty years previously.

"Café Neko. Aah." He pointed in the direction of the main road. "Aah. Left. One, two hundred metre." He bowed, and his eyes wrinkled with pleasure at his bilingual achievement.

I beamed back at him, bowed, said 'Arigatō' many times, and we parted company.

He called after us in Japanese. I stopped and turned.

"Level two. Aah."

"Level two. Second floor. Arigatō." We bowed at each other again, and I had a brief moment of sadness as I realised the connection I'd made with this helpful fellow human could never be continued.

Following his instructions, we marched left towards the built-up area. I repeatedly turned around to ensure my family followed me, and I couldn't understand why they didn't walk faster.

"Did he say one hundred metres or two hundred metres?" I asked Candi.

"Both."

"Oh. We must've walked two hundred metres by now."

"Here's a hotel," said Fiona. Let's ask in reception. She pushed a glass door and entered a foyer completely bereft of anything except some plastic pot plants and a man with a suitcase talking on a telephone.

"Um, there isn't a reception," said Candi.

"Maybe it's on another floor?" suggested Ellie.

"We don't have time for this." I scraped my hand through my hair then glanced at my watch. "The café must be here somewhere. Didn't the crossing man say the second floor? Keep walking."

"Could we investigate this shopping arcade?" asked Candi, pointing at a five-storey, modern building showcasing windows brimming with designer gear.

"No, we could not," I said. "Maybe afterwards."

"But we still have twenty minutes until our capybara appointment."

"I know, but we haven't pinpointed its location yet."

Shops selling the regulation suburban products bordered the pavement: groceries, independent clothes stores, magazines. We marched past all of them.

278

"Dad, I can see it," said Ellie.

"Where? Quick." I followed her gaze and strode faster.

She pointed further along the street. "There. Café Neko. It has a cartoon of the capybara."

I sprinted towards where she'd indicated, stopped and stood with my hands on my hips.

Café Neko.

My watch said 5:17 p.m.

A light shone from the second floor.

Here we were. Within metres of my bucket list goal.

My dream.

An animal I'd wanted to meet all my life.

I breathed out. We'd made it.

"Press floor two," I said to Ellie. I beamed. "Capybara floor."

The lift jolted upwards, and the doors opened into a foyer the size of an old-fashioned English telephone box. A sign said, 'Remove Shoe Before Enter'.

"Dad, put on these slippers," said Candi, handing me plastic-wrapped, linen moccasins. "They won't let you in without them."

"Okay, okay." I tugged my shoes off and bumped elbows and bottoms with my family, as we all tried to swap our footwear simultaneously in the tiny area.

"And sanitise your hands," said Ellie. She held out a small, transparent bottle and squirted liquid into my palms.

I rubbed my hands together as if I were washing them after using the toilet.

"And put your face mask on," said Fiona.

"Bloody hell." I inhaled as I twanged the mask around my ears, and it pushed into my mouth. "Any other rituals to observe before we enter?"

"Dad," said Candi. "I saw it."

"What?"

"The capybara. Through the glass door."

"Ring the bell. Quick."

Candi pushed the buzzer. A young lady swung the door open and bowed four times, once for each of us. She smiled behind her mask and said "Konbanwa."

"Konbanwa," I replied. I could hardly breathe. "Prior family. We booked for 5:30." I glanced at my watch and hoped she'd consider 5:21 acceptable.

A laminated, English-language document introduced her as Ayane and laid out capybara-interacting regulations, including a request not to frighten the animal by approaching it from above; to always bend to its level. I would've stood on my head if demanded. The card also explained the capybara was female, named Kikurage-chan, or Ki-chan, for short.

The lady straightened her arm in a graceful, universal invitation to enter, and we stepped through the pearly gates into heaven.

I'd glimpsed capybaras at zoos.

I'd seen photographs of them in books, magazines and online.

I'd watched television documentaries presented by Attenborough-wannabes, where they'd explained the dangers of life as a huge, tasty vegetarian in an anaconda-infested, South American jungle.

I'd never met one.

Until today.

My body froze; I stared and forgot to blink.

The size of a large, solid dog; brown, with bristly fur, stumpy legs and tiny ears, the capybara amused herself by chewing a door frame with her strong incisors, topped by her flat-fronted, snub nose.

I immediately fell in love with her dark, elliptical, Barbie-doll eyes.

The lady produced a bowl of lettuce leaves, bowed and invited us to feed Ki-chan. She handed the bowl to Ellie.

In a perfect, Instagram-worthy world, Ellie would've held one end of a lettuce leaf and the capybara would've gently nibbled the other end as if she were a tame bunny, while we all smiled happily and took photos.

What actually happened was: the capybara lurched at Ellie, upended the bowl and covered the floor with greenery, which she then proceeded to vacuum up like a cow.

I squatted, wide-eyed.

"Dad," said Candi. "Look at this cat. It likes to sit across your shoulders."

"Very nice." I waved Candi away. Cats held no interest.

"Take my photo," I said. "Take loads with me and Ki-chan."

Fiona grinned at my euphoria. "Finally, you got your Christmas present."

I crouched awkwardly with the capybara as Fiona snapped pictures.

Ki-Chan ignored me.

Should I do something to engage her? But what?

Thirty minutes in the presence of an animal I'd wanted to meet all my life, and here we were, and I didn't know what to do. I perched on a seat, and the capybara ambled away.

Chasing her around the café possibly wasn't correct capybara-etiquette.

The lady brought another bowl. She laid it in front of Ki-chan, who placed one webbed foot on the edge and flipped it over, so the floor was covered in small, black pellets.

"She's not the tidiest of eaters, is she?" said Ellie.

Ki-chan objected to this observation.

SKREK

"Was it Ki-chan who made that sound? Or one of the cats?" I looked around to see where the noise had originated, as it didn't seem to come directly from the capybara.

SKRAK

"It's the capybara, Dad."

SKREETTER

"She sounds like a parrot with laryngitis."

I sprawled beside her while she nibbled.

"Don't lie on the ground," said Fiona. "You'll make your new rugby jersey dirty."

"I don't care. We can buy another rugby jersey; I might never recline next to a capybara again. Take more photos."

I placed my hand on Ki-chan's scrubbing brush fur. A warmth proliferated through my body, and every other human and cat in the world blurred into the background.

The capybara shuffled in a semicircle and presented her backside to the camera.

"I'm not sure that's the best view," I said. "Here, I'll move."

I stroked her like a dog and scratched behind her ears. Ki-chan closed her eyes and bent her head.

My stomach fluttered, and a tingling spread from my chest towards my fingers. I wanted to pick her up and cuddle her, but she probably wouldn't have enjoyed that. She was also probably too heavy.

Definitely not capybara-etiquette.

"Dad," said Ellie, from under a fluffy tabby, "this sign says we can adopt the cats. Could we take this one home?"

"Does it say whether we could adopt Ki-chan?"

"I think the adoption thing's for locals," said Fiona. "Australian Customs might look at you strangely if you turned up with a fully grown capybara under your arm."

Candi scratched the capybara at the base of her tail. She recommenced her inspection of the scattered pellets, then lay down flat against a wooden bench.

I cautiously approached and lay beside her. She didn't withdraw, so I slowly raised my arm, and took a capybara-selfie.

And another one.

And another one.

And another one hundred.

The girls played with the cats.

Ki-chan stood on her four, stumpy, webbed feet and returned to the upturned food bowl. A cat jumped on my shoulders.

"Dad, the cats need attention too," said Candi.

I half-heartedly patted the cat.

The staff member filled a large tub from a tap.

Fiona lay a hand on my arm. "It's time to go. The café's closing."

I stooped, stroked the capybara's head, and said goodbye.

Goodbye to Ki-chan.

Goodbye to the animal I'd wanted to meet all my life.

My eyes watered as I turned to the lady and asked, "Does Ki-chan have a bath every night?"

She bowed and shook her head, in a gesture I now knew meant her inability to understand me embarrassed her. I typed into Google translate and showed her my phone. She grinned behind her mask and nodded. She typed back.

>>>Yes. Ki-chan has a bath every night. She loves her bath. I am boiling the water now.

I hoped 'boiling' was a translation error, as I felt capybaras probably desired the water no hotter than lukewarm, but I appreciated her care for Ki-chan, who seemed to have adjusted to captivity well.

The pavement outside Capy Neko café thronged with evening commuters.

"Let's visit the shopping centre across the road," said Ellie. "Last-minute purchasing."

"Yes. I need food," said Candi. "And free wifi to upload my cat photos."

"Hang on," I said. "Stop."

I swivelled on my heels and stared up at the second-floor window, where I knew Ki-chan enjoyed her evening bath. "Pause, everyone. I've ticked off a bucket list item, and I need to reflect."

"While you're pausing, we'll try on clothes," said Fiona. "Join us when you've finished reflecting."

The three of them waited for the tweety-bird signal, then crossed the road and entered the shopping mall.

My hands shoved in my pockets, I gazed up at the café window, took deep breaths and savoured the moment.

Fiona, Candi and Ellie stripped garments from the rails and played musical doors with the fitting rooms. They called to each other and compared various bargains they'd discovered. Empty coat hangers clattered on the floor as they tested tops, coats and jeans.

I placed my palms against the inside of the clothes shop's second-floor window, stared across the busy main street of Kichijōji and watched as the lights extinguished in Capy Neko café.

I wondered how the young lady bathed and dried the capybara by herself; she was a large animal for the slight woman to deal with.

My nose chilled as I kissed the glass.

I wondered what Ki-Chan slept on.

I wondered how she coped in Tokyo's distant suburbs, a long way from the jungles of South America, a place she'd never seen and would never see.

I wondered if she felt superior to her feline café-mates; a gigantic, vegetarian rodent surrounded by tiny, carnivorous predators.

I wondered if Ki-Chan was lonely.

Lonely without other capybaras to squeak with.

"Dad," said a voice behind me. "D'you like this top?"

"Very nice," I said to Ellie.

"Could I buy these earrings?" asked Candi. "They're five hundred yen."

"Sure."

Fiona tapped me, and I glanced over my shoulder. "I thought I might purchase this jumper. It goes with the jeans I bought in England. What d'you think?"

"Lovely."

I turned back, stared across the street at the dark windows of the second-floor cafe, blew a kiss and said a silent Sayōnara.

38. SAYŌNARA

Twenty-six nursery rhymes and two complicated line changes later we lugged our multiple shopping carriers into the ryokan.

"It's 10:30," said Fiona. "Ellie's exhausted. So am I. We're going straight to bed."

"I'll be there in a minute; I want to ask about check out."

It was a different receptionist this evening. She smiled and bowed. "Konbanwa. How can I help?"

"We're checking out tomorrow, but our flight's not until the evening. Could we leave our bags with you during the day? There's, um, a lot of them."

"No problem. You may leave them here." She pointed to a vacant area of the black, wooden floor behind me. "Is there anything else you need? Maybe another mattress?"

"I beg your pardon?"

"Would you like another mattress?"

I puffed out my cheeks like a hamster. "Yes, please. I'd love another mattress. I didn't realise it was an option."

"Many western guests prefer two. They find thin, Japanese mattresses too uncomfortable. I'll bring it upstairs."

"Um, gosh." I smiled and nodded. "Thank you."

She bowed, and I bowed.

Fiona lay in bed with a book as I bounced into our room.

"Guess what?" I pulled off my shoes.

"What? Ssh, I'm almost asleep."

"They're giving me another mattress. D'you want one too?"

"I'm fine. Why are they doing that?"

"The receptionist said their Western guests often prefer two. I wish I'd known when we arrived. My back wouldn't be in agony now."

'The Skye Boat Song' serenaded us off the train for our line change at Asakusa station. We dragged our bags up the stairs into the ticket hall.

Groups of passengers wheeled black cases in a mass trundling noise across the concourse. Station announcements sounded, preceded by electronic, tinny jingles. I rubbed my chin and glanced around for any symbol resembling a train going to an airport.

"Dad," said Candi. "Those machines say airport tickets." She pointed at three large consoles against a far wall.

A station employee grasping a clipboard approached and bowed. "Hello. Do you need airport train?"

"Yes, four of us." I brandished my credit card.

She bowed. "Sorry, sir. We do not take card. Only cash."

"You're kidding. For the airport train?"

"Very sorry, sir." She held out an arm. "ATM this way, sir." She instructed a colleague, who allowed me through the barriers without a ticket.

The ATM wasn't friendly, and no helpful post office lady stood by to point at the correct controls. Although I successfully commenced the transaction by pressing a Union Jack button, the machine forced me to withdraw a minimum of ten thousand yen, which meant I'd have oodles of Japanese cash to dispose of in the airport shops buying pointless chocolate and souvenirs. The ATM also joyfully demanded five hundred yen for the privilege of withdrawing the notes; cash I'd never wanted to withdraw. I gritted my teeth and persevered with the electronic negotiations.

The station lady escorted me back through the ticket barriers. "You want slow train or express train?"

"What's the difference?"

"Express train three thousand yen each. Thirty minutes no stops. Slow train one thousand, two hundred yen each. Two hours and stops everywhere."

We'll take the slow train," I said, fanning out the ten thousand yen and performing rapid mental arithmetic. "We have four hours until our flight departs."

She showed me which buttons to press, and I inserted five thousand yen, which bought me the customary four small pieces of card.

"Take the second train, platform two. The Keisei Main Line for Narita Airport. Not the first train; the Keisei Access Express for Narita. That is fast train. You do not have tickets for that."

In this country where up to four railway stations possessed the same name, I wasn't surprised to hear two rail lines shared a similar name as well.

The Keisei Access Express arrived, and the guard and driver exchanged white-gloved bows. Smartly dressed professional-looking airport passengers boarded, towing their shiny, Samsonite luggage.

We dragged our battered suitcases and bulging holdalls onto the second train, and the carriages began a lengthy clackety-clack through Tokyo's extensive suburbs. None of our fellow passengers shared our airport destination. They all grasped standard commuter accoutrements: a briefcase, a handbag, an overcoat, a mobile phone.

Ellie slept against Fiona. Candi lay on me.

I averted my gaze from the endless minuscule, crammed-in houses, clasped my hands in front of me and closed my eyes.

Had we achieved our holiday goals?

I wondered whether any storage remained in Candi's phone, and whether her friends' hunger for Snapchat posts of Christmas Markets had been satiated.

My memory of Ellie's pleasure at finding a redheaded bagpiper fluttered a brief smile across my face.

The size and quantity of luggage blocking the train's aisle testified to Fiona's successful shopping expeditions.

An hour passed, and fields bordered the line, backdropped by small hills and trees. Distance between stations increased. The doors opened, and a group of three Arabic men boarded, conversing loudly in their own language. They were dressed in manual workers' orange tunics, and I realised they were the first non-Japanese people I'd seen, apart from obvious tourists. I recalled Candi teaching me Japan was a nation state, populated almost entirely by people of Japanese origin. I closed my eyes and returned to my thoughts.

Many things about Japan surprised me.

I never demand people in other countries speak my language, and I always learn a few words of theirs before I visit. But, in Japan, many people spoke no English at all. Not one word. And the bigger surprise—this applied to foreign money exchange clerks, and railway station information staff. I'd never used Google Translate so much. The corners of my mouth turned up, as I recalled my beautiful slice-of-life encounter with the helpful school crossing man.

So many places refused credit cards. A chain of ice-cream shops, a concession in a department store, even buying the airport train tickets. I'd always imagined Japan to be a super-technological, highly digitalised society.

My enchantment as station attendants and train drivers bowed to each other when the train approached the platform and again as it departed. Construction traffic workers bowed as they briefly detained us while supervising a reversing truck. Even advertisements thanking consumers for buying Toyota cars showed a cartoon figure bowing. I hadn't anticipated this omnipresent and deferential culture.

I'd miss Japan very much. We'd barely scratched the surface of this unique country, and I mentally planned another visit to experience more. A lot more.

Plus, I had another reason to return.

The most important reason.

Someone I wanted to visit again and again.

My friend, Ki-Chan.

Ki-Chan, the Christmas capybara.

THE END

Ki-Chan and Simon.

EPILOGUE:
CAPYBARAS AND THE JAPANESE

The wonderful, ebullient capybara is quite simply a gigantic mouse. Or hamster, Guinea pig, whatever. It's the largest rodent in the world by a long way, standing half a metre tall at the shoulder and is phenomenally cute.

I first fell in love with them after Gerald Durrell described the capture of the waterhaas (water horse), as they are locally known in parts of South America, an explanation which had teenage-me in hysterics reading about the animal enjoying playing tunes on its cage wires with its strong front teeth.

They're social animals, living in small groups of around twenty, and seem to be quite happy in the company of different species, such as cats or humans. Found in every South American country except Chile, they inhabit dense, swampy jungle, love swimming and can submerge without breathing for up to five minutes. They're even able to sleep underwater, with their noses poking out so they can breathe. Their favourite food is grass and water plants (although apparently they also eat their own poo. I'm sure Ki-Chan was far too polite to do that.)

Capybaras aren't endangered, and they adapt well to captivity. They're docile, known for their gentle temperament and can become quite friendly with humans if raised in captivity from a young age.

Capybaras became popular in Japan due to the cartoon character Kapibara-san created by a company called Tryworks in 2006. Cuddly, stumpy-legged, round-nosed, little-eared Kapibara-sans appeared on T-shirts, books, pencil cases, socks, bread buns and plush toys, and soon everyone was in love with them.

Real live capybaras arrived in Japan considerably earlier, in the 1960s, when Japanese zoos imported them. At first, they didn't stand out amongst the other exotic more impressive big cats and giant African herbivores, but then in 1982, the Izu Shaboten zoo began allowing its capybaras to bathe in onsen, the traditional Japanese hot springs. The Japanese population fell in love with the sight of these animals enjoying the water, and their popularity was assured. There are now around five hundred capybaras in zoos around Japan. The odd one seems to have found its way into an animal café…

PLEASE REVIEW
A CAPYBARA FOR CHRISTMAS

Please consider leaving a review on Amazon to let other readers know how much you enjoyed *A Capybara for Christmas*.

Even if you didn't buy the book from Amazon, you can still leave a review there if you have a valid Amazon account.

Reviews help authors too, and I read every one with interest and gratitude.

Thanks so much, it means a lot to me.
Simon

ALSO BY SIMON:
THE COCONUT WIRELESS

When Simon and Fiona embark on a quest to track down the Queen of Tonga, they have no idea they'll end up marooned on a desert island.

No idea they'll encounter an undiscovered tribe, rescue a drowning actress, learn jungle survival from a commando, and attend cultural ceremonies few Westerners have seen.

As they find out who hooks up, who breaks up, who cracks up, and who throws up, will they fulfil Simon's ambition to see the queen, or will they be distracted by insomniac chickens, grunting wild piglets, and the easy-going Tongan lifestyle?

Read the first few chapters FREE by visiting:
getbook.at/thecoconutwireless

ALSO BY SIMON:
THE SCENICLAND RADIO

When English city boy Simon follows his girlfriend across the world to her family farm in remotest New Zealand, he has no idea he'll be force-fed a meal of beetle larva, get pushed off the road by half a house, and be inspected by indignant penguins and flattened by a giant leaf-blower.

As he poisons the milk, dive-bombs the bulls, and loses the herd of cows in a river, will he ever learn to be a farmer, or will he have to stop impersonating a country boy, and return to London?

**Read the first few chapters FREE by visiting:
mybook.to/scenicland**

ALSO BY SIMON:
THE POMEGRANATE BUSKER

When London boy Simon dreams of becoming a New Zealand rock star, he has no idea he'll duet with a suspected murderer, model for posters with a dairy cow, accidentally present the weather on the radio and be upstaged by an apple crumble.

As he struggles to impersonate Elvis, forgets the most important birthday song and scares away a hen party, will he ever realise his rock star ambitions, or will he have to pack away his guitar and abandon his dreams forever?

Read the first few chapters FREE by visiting:
mybook.to/pomegranate

ALSO BY SIMON:
THE ANTICLOCKWISE PROPOSAL

When Simon embarks on an around-the-world quest to find the perfect engagement ring, he has no idea he'll re-enact a celebrity double murder, check into a Chinese torture facility, star as James Bond in an underwater movie and take part in an opium den toilet-paper hunt.

As he fights off Cantonese Pavarottis, Chihuahua-brandishing socialites, dodgy diamond dealers and hen-pecked secret agents, will he ever persuade his girlfriend to accept his proposal, or will he have to abandon his plans and remain a bachelor forever?

**Read the first few chapters FREE by visiting:
mybook.to/anticlockwise**

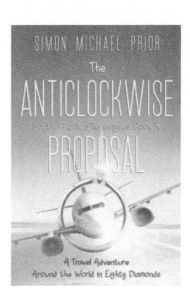

ALSO BY SIMON:
AN ENGLISHMAN IN NEW YORK

Have you ever wanted a first-hand glimpse into post-war 1940s New York?

When 21-year-old John Miskin Prior travelled by ship to New York in 1948, he had no idea he was going to meet and dine with the Roosevelts and the Rockefellers. No idea he would be among the first ever to see 'South Pacific' and 'Death of a Salesman'. No idea he would witness Truman's election victory, so unexpected, the newspapers were reprinted.

This eyewitness account of an English student living in New York for the incredible year of 1948 – 49 has been collated from his letters discovered after his death, and forms a unique account of the period.

Read the first few chapters FREE by visiting:
mybook.to/englishman

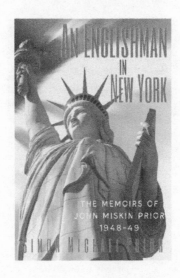

DISCLAIMER

This is a work in the genre creative non-fiction. I have tried to recreate events, locales and conversations from my memories of them. To maintain their anonymity, in some instances I have changed the names of individuals and places. Some characters in this book are composites, comprised of more than one person I met. I may have changed some identifying characteristics and details such as physical properties, occupations and places of residence. Any mistakes are all my own work. SMP.

ABOUT THE AUTHOR

Simon Michael Prior insists on inflicting all aspects of life on himself so that his readers can enjoy learning about his latest trip / experience / disaster / emotional breakdown (insert phrase of your choice).

During his extended adolescence, now over forty years long, he has lived on two boats and sunk one of them; sold houses, street signs, Indian food and paper bags for a living; visited almost fifty countries and lived in three; qualified as a scuba divemaster; nearly killed himself learning to wakeboard; trained as a search and rescue skipper with the Coast Guard, and built his own house without the benefit of an instruction manual.

Simon is as amazed as anyone that the house is still standing, and he now lives in it by the sea with his wife and twin daughters, where he spends his time regurgitating his experiences on paper before he has so many more that he forgets them.

Website: **simonmichaelprior.com**

Email: **simon@simonmichaelprior.com**

Facebook: **@simonmichaelprior**

Instagram: **@simonmichaelprior**

If you would like to receive a regular newsletter about Simon and his writing, and be the first to find out about new releases, please sign up to his mailing list here:

simonmichaelprior.com

ACKNOWLEDGEMENTS

A big thank you to Victoria Twead and all the members of the Facebook group 'We Love Memoirs', for befriending me, encouraging me, educating me, reassuring me, and driving me forward.

This book wouldn't have been possible without the help of the following people: The wonderful beta readers: Alison Ripley-Cubitt, Alyson Sheldrake, Julie Haigh, Kellie McIntyre and Pauline Armstrong; your feedback improved the final result so much.

Thank you to Andrew Freudenberg for giving me the inspiration.

Thank you to Victoria Twead, Matthew J Holmes, Meg LaTorre, Craig Martelle, Angela Ackerman, Becca Puglisi, David Gaughran and Dave Chesson for informative courses, tips and useful tools.

Thank you to Jeff Bezos, for giving independent authors a platform on which to publish our writing.

And thank you so much to Fiona, Elloise and Candice. I couldn't have done it without you.

WE LOVE MEMOIRS

Made in United States
North Haven, CT
13 December 2023

45657102R00182